PHYSICIAN to the CHILDREN

Dr. Béla Schick

The Schick test to determine susceptibility to
diphtheria is familiar to everyone, but how many
people know about the man for whom this important discovery was named? While Dr. Schick
gained world fame for his work in the prevention of diphtheria, he was particularly concerned
with the diseases of children, choosing to work
in the tragedy-filled children's ward of a hospital, rather than in a branch of medicine that
would give him security. Through his development of the science of pediatrics, doctors gained
a new insight into the vital needs and special
care of children. Here is the story of a boy who
fought poverty, prejudice, jealousy and emerged
a crusader and humanitarian who is today re-
vered by everyone in the medical profession.

BOOKS BY IRIS NOBLE

Biographies

CLARENCE DARROW: Defense Attorney
THE COURAGE OF DR. LISTER
THE DOCTOR WHO DARED: William Osler
EGYPT'S QUEEN: Cleopatra
EMPRESS OF ALL RUSSIA: Catherine the Great
FIRST WOMAN AMBULANCE SURGEON:
  Emily Barringer
GREAT LADY OF THE THEATRE: Sarah Bernhardt
JOSEPH PULITZER: Front Page Pioneer
NELLIE BLY: First Woman Reporter
NURSE AROUND THE WORLD: Alice Fitzgerald
PHYSICIAN TO THE CHILDREN: Dr. Bela Schick
WILLAM SHAKESPEARE

Novels

MEGAN
ONE GOLDEN SUMMER
STRANGER NO MORE
THE TENDER PROMISE

PHYSICIAN
to the
CHILDREN
Dr. Béla Schick

by

Iris Noble

Julian Messner
New York

Published by Julian Messner
Division of Pocket Books, Inc.
8 West 40th Street, New York 10018

Second printing, 1966

Printed in the United States of America
Library of Congress Catalog Card No. 63-16792

Acknowledgment

Grateful acknowledgment is given to Dr. and Mrs. Béla Schick for their help both in correspondence and in personal interviews with the author of this book. In addition, I am deeply indebted to Dr. Anne Topper, Dr. Murray Peshkin, Dr. Jerome S. Leopold, Dr. Camille Kereszturi Cayley and Dr. Alla Dunewitz, who gave so generously of their time to supply research material and anecdotes.

I should also like to thank the Mendocino County Library Demonstration which services this coastal area of California by bookmobile, for their extraordinary promptness in securing for me medical books and pamphlets long out of print.

PHYSICIAN to the CHILDREN

Dr. Béla Schick

1

"Are you sick?" The train conductor bent over the boy who sat crouched down in the plush seat of the railroad car.

"I'm all right," the boy answered. He didn't look all right; when he turned his face to the conductor it was a shocking sight. The eyes were swollen so nearly shut there were only slits for him to see out of, and the skin on his forehead and cheekbones was puffed and red. "I think a bee or a wasp stung me." He bit his lip. He was twelve years old and determined not to cry, in spite of the pain.

"Ach!" The conductor was sympathetic. "Never have I seen such a swelling from an insect sting." He shook his head in wonder. "But why are you on this train? Why aren't you home? You didn't board this train at Vienna. You must have got on at Graz. Where are you going?"

"To Boglar, in Hungary, to see my uncle. He's a doctor," explained the boy, letting his head sink back onto the coolness of the windowpane.

The conductor started to go on. He stopped abruptly. "To Boglar? Then you must mean Dr. Telegdi; he is the only doctor there. Ach, no wonder you come all the way from Graz just to see him. He is the best in Hungary. All the rich

9

people go to the summer resort of Boglar and I hear them talking about how wonderful he is." He patted the boy's shoulder. "If he is your uncle, he will take care of you."

Despite his suffering, the boy smiled. Then the throbbing around his eyes became worse and he peered, in anxiety, at the passing landscape. Would they never finish riding through Austria and pass the border into Hungary? Only twenty miles more—only ten—he counted each mile. Finally, they were in Hungary and there at last, through the trees, came the first glimpse of the blue lake and the white cottages, the big hotels of the summer resort of Boglar.

He was the first one out when the trained stopped. He tumbled down the steps, straight into the arms of his Uncle Sigismund Telegdi.

"Béla, you poor boy!" His uncle pronounced the name 'Bayla,' in the correct Hungarian way. "Let me see you." He gently tilted his nephew's chin and studied his injured eyes. After a few seconds, he spoke with confidence. "It will be all right. I'll have you fixed up in no time."

His uncle's horse and carriage took them to the house, which was also his office and consulting rooms. In the study lined with medical books on the shelves and disorderly with medical journals piled on the tables, Béla sat in an old, worn leather chair while his uncle mixed several mysterious powders together and ground them in a stone mortar.

Already Béla was feeling better. He loved this study. There was the flicker of logs burning in the fireplace, the soft glow from the gas lamps, and the sharp, medicinal odors of lotions and herb roots. It was a smell that pleased him.

While the doctor worked, he talked. "How is your father?

And Janka, your mother, is she well? What does she call the new baby?"

"Ilona," Béla answered. "They are all well and send you their love, Uncle Sigismund. Frieda thinks that Ilona is a new doll for her to play with, and Richard has his hands full, keeping her away from Mamma and the baby."

"Well," his uncle said, smiling, "Frieda is only a year old, remember. I suppose Richard thinks he is too big to mind his sister, and I suppose Serena is too busy thinking of courtship and her own future babies to want to be bothered."

Serena was Béla's half sister. His father's first wife had died very young. He had remarried some years later, and Serena seemed to Béla so much older than himself that she belonged with the adults, not with the children. Richard was one year his senior.

"Lie down on this couch," Dr. Telegdi ordered. He took some of his powder preparation, mixed it with a lotion and applied it to the swelling on the boy's face. It was deliciously wet and cool. Béla gave a contented little groan, in relief, and sank back on the couch. Dr. Telegdi bandaged his eyes and head.

"So Janka sent you all this way so that I could take care of you. That is good." The doctor was fond of his sister, whose real name was Johanna, but who was nicknamed 'Janka.' She was fair-haired and blue-eyed; sweet, and charming; more important, she let him see as much of this favorite nephew as he wanted to. "Try to sleep now."

"I can't sleep," came Béla's muffled voice.

"No? Shall I talk to you? Very well; you are always my best audience. A lonely doctor needs to talk." He settled himself in a chair near the couch and lit his pipe. "I wish I could

tell you why an insect's sting makes only a tiny swelling on
some people, while it does such terrible things to other people.
We don't know, but we will someday, Béla. We are living
in a wonderful age! All these past centuries doctors have tried
to cure infections and disease without knowing what caused
them. Think of it—when I was a student my teachers had
never heard of bacteria or germs. They knew nothing of the
principles of antiseptics."

Béla caught his uncle's excitement. "That is all changed
now, isn't it?"

"It is all changed. Or beginning to change—" the doctor
corrected himself. "I have been privileged to go back to Budapest for postgraduate work. I've had the chance to study this
new science of bacteriology. Bacteria, germs, microbes—call
them what you will—Louis Pasteur's discovery of them has
opened up the medical book of knowledge to us. I studied his
theories, and Robert Koch's and Joseph Lister's. Oh, there
are doctors in Vienna and Budapest and in Graz who will tell
you that Pasteur and Lister are crazy. Don't you believe it."

Béla heard him push back his chair, go to the hall door and
call: "Maria! Bring hot chocolate and biscuits, will you,
please?"

He returned to his chair and Béla could hear the creaking
sound of the leather as he sat down. "Every month, my boy,
I read these medical journals," he said. "Every month, new
discoveries. We know now the bacteria that causes anthrax
and the one that causes tuberculosis, but there is so much to
be learned. When you are a doctor—"

"Papa says no," interrupted Béla. "He says I mustn't ever
talk to him about being a doctor. He forbids it."

There was a silence, then Uncle Sigismund said: "Try to understand your father. He loves you. He thinks he knows what is best for you. He tried to become a doctor when he was a young man. He tried and he failed. He does not want that to happen to you."

When the servant Maria brought in the chocolate she informed the doctor, "The maid of Frau von Dorst is waiting outside, Herr Doctor. Will you go to see her mistress tonight?"

"Tell her," said Dr. Telegdi, crisply, "that I cannot see her tonight. I will come in the morning."

"But," protested the maid, "Frau von Dorst is rich and powerful!

"She is rich and pampered and if she didn't eat so many pastries and drink so much schnapps, she wouldn't be sick," he retorted. When the maid had gone, he chuckled. "I scandalize Maria. She cannot understand why I treat the poor the same as I do the rich. She is certain something awful will happen to me if I don't drop everything to do the bidding of every silly Frau von Dorst."

He guided Béla's hands around the chocolate cup and helped him sit up and drink it. "The day after tomorrow I am going away on my monthly trip through one of my three districts. Would you like to go?"

"May I? That would be marvelous. Don't I have to go back to school right away?" Behind his bandage Béla could feel that the swelling was going down; the skin was not so tight; the throbbing was growing less and less.

"A few more days won't hurt your schooling. I hear you have excellent grades." The doctor laughed. "Perhaps I can teach you what your school can't—about medicine. Shall I lecture to you as if I were your professor? Very well, listen. This is 1889. A little more than twenty-five years ago a man named Louis Pasteur discovered bacteria."

"Was he a doctor?" asked Béla.

"Don't interrupt your professor. No, he was a French chemist. He looked under a microscope and he found tiny, living one-celled organisms which he called 'bacteria' or 'germs.' These little things were alive. Oh, they didn't talk or walk around or drink chocolate, but they were just as much alive as you are. These germs have the power of motion— although some have to be sort of pushed along; they eat, they digest, they breed."

"They are what cause the infectious diseases, aren't they, Uncle Sigismund?"

"Yes, but there are bacteria which are not harmful, too. Those were the ones Pasteur found first. He discovered that it was bacteria which made beer out of certain other substances, and wine out of grapes. They made ferment. Pasteur told the world about his discovery, but most people just laughed at him. There were a few who didn't—an Englishman named Joseph Lister, who knew immediately that it was those same bacteria which were getting into wounds and into the cuts that a surgeon's knife makes, causing infection and death. There was a German, Robert Koch, who read what Pasteur had done and then discovered the tuberculosis bacteria, and two other Germans, Friedrich Löffler and Edwin Klebs, who worked together to discover the bacteria which was causing diphtheria. So it has gone. Every year I read in my medical journals of some new discovery. Béla, the book of medicine was a child's primer when I studied. Now it is as if we have the real book in our hands and every day we turn a new page to a new discovery." He said, softly: "Béla?"

The relief from pain had caught up with the boy, and in spite of his interest in what Uncle Sigismund was saying, he had fallen soundly asleep.

Two days later, when they were riding in their carriage on Dr. Telegdi's district tour, his uncle finished telling him about Louis Pasteur.

In 1881, eight years before, Louis Pasteur had proved that bacteria could be harmful in causing disease; he also proved that man could use the bacteria to prevent disease. Sheep died of a disease called anthrax. By injecting sheep with a very weak dose of the anthrax bacteria, and then a second and a third dose, each time stronger, Louis Pasteur claimed the sheep would get so used to the bacteria that they would become immune and could then take a strong, killing dose of it without harm.

"Picture it for yourself!" Dr. Telegdi exclaimed, slapping the reins on the horse's back to hurry him up. "The test was held on a farm. Louis Pasteur and his assistants were there; so were the Melun Agricultural Society and also physicians who had scoffed at him. On this farm were twenty-four sheep, one goat and six cows, which had already received Pasteur's three weak doses. Now, on this day he would inject them with a massive dose. At the same time he would give the same dose to an equal number of animals who had never had any injections before. What do you think happened?"

Béla could see it all—the farm and the man with the injection needle, and the animals, and all those people watching.

He felt himself grow tense. "I don't know. What did happen?"

"The very next morning they found all the animals he had previously injected alive and healthy. One was slightly ill but not from anthrax. The rest of the animals, who had not had the weak doses and were therefore not inoculated and immune—all were dead!"

While Béla was still marveling and thinking about this, their horse turned a corner and they came trotting into a small village. Dr. Telegdi pulled up the horse at the village square, around which were placed a church, a combination post office and store, several taverns, a little shabby building that was a schoolhouse.

Béla could hardly see any of these, so crowded was the square with people who surged forward as soon as they saw the carriage. "The doctor has come!" they cried.

A young man proudly held the horse's head; another reached out to carry the doctor's bag. Old men and women pressed forward, seized Dr. Telegdi's hand and kissed it. Young women came shyly up and held their infants in their arms, waiting patiently for their turn. A table was set up and a stool brought for the beloved doctor to sit on.

Béla was astounded and very proud at this reception for his uncle. He hadn't realized that others loved him as much as he did.

A mother came, crying, and the crowd made way for her. The child she carried was screaming with pain. "Please, Herr Doctor, help my baby. There is something in his eye; it is killing him!" she implored.

"Hold him quietly, while I look." Dr. Telegdi bent over

the child, but the mother was in such a nervous state that she could not control the baby's threshing arms and legs. "Here—Béla—come and see if you can hold him more firmly." There was an impatient, urgent note in his uncle's voice and Béla stepped forward without hesitation, taking the baby from his mother.

At the touch of the small body in his arms, something was immediately communicated to Béla Schick. He knew, without question, that the child was more frightened than hurt; that the mother's fear had been felt by the infant and was making him frantic. Béla found himself making soothing strokes on the child's arm; talking to him in a calm and gentle way; holding him firmly but not in a tight grip.

The child relaxed. His screaming died down to a whimper, and he turned his face up to follow Béla's comforting words. As he did so Dr. Telegdi quickly examined the inflamed eye and as quickly found the piece of metal which had lodged in it.

Almost the second the cause was removed, the child stopped his whimpering and smiled. Béla handed him back to his mother, whose face was covered with tears of joy. "Thank you, Herr Doctor, thank you. We can pay this time—will an egg be enough? Or a loaf of my fresh-baked bread?"

"Give the egg to your child—for a treat. Give me the bread. I remember; it is very good bread." Dr. Telegdi smiled at her and turned to the next patient, to examine a festering sore on his leg.

Four hours the doctor worked and still the patients came with every kind of illness. He lanced boils, gave powders for stomachs, sewed up cuts on foreheads and arms and legs, pre-

scribed diets for colicky babies, proudly examined the new
and well babies he had delivered the month before. He had
brought a cane for one old, crippled woman and gave it to her
for a present. He left the square and went into homes to see
the bedridden.

What Béla saw that day made a profound impression upon
him. Medicine was not just glamorous stories of great men
like Pasteur. It was also the humble service of a man like Dr.
Telegdi, who could have been rich had he gone to a city
where wealthy patients would have flocked to his office, but
who preferred Boglar and the villagers who could pay him
with a loaf of bread.

When at last he had seen everyone in that town, Dr. Telegdi
and Béla drove away to visit a farmhouse in the hills. "Tell
me, Béla, how did you quiet that child so easily? It was like a
miracle."

"I remembered that I was afraid when my eye was stung.
The more afraid I was, the more it hurt. The moment I
reached Boglar I forgot to be afraid and the pain was not so
bad. Somehow I just knew that baby was more frightened
than hurt. I thought to myself, if I were a baby and my mother
was crying and carrying on, wouldn't I be terrified?"

His uncle reached over and squeezed his hand. "You will
make a fine doctor. You have that extra kind of feeling, to
sense what a patient is feeling. It is easy with an adult. They
tell you they are afraid, or where the pain is. Children are
more difficult because the little things can't always tell you.
If you can understand a child as you did today, that is a very
precious talent."

They came into the yard of the farmhouse. A gray-faced

father was waiting for them at the gate. The mother hovered in the doorway, wringing her hands in her apron. "Thank God you have come, Doctor," said the man. "The girl—our Sophie—is suffocating with a terrible gray stuff in her throat!"

"Diphtheria," Dr. Telegdi muttered. He said to Béla: "You stay in the carriage. If it is diphtheria it is contagious."

Béla waited. It was evening now. He lit the lantern on the carriage and snuggled down inside a warm robe. He dozed off, awaking only when his uncle shook him.

One glance at his face and Béla knew that little Sophie was dead. He heard weeping from the farmhouse. The father stood by the carriage, saying, "You did your best, Herr Doctor. I thank you. Would a basket of apples—?"

"Keep them. Don't pay me. Only do one thing for me," said his uncle, in a harsh, agonized voice. "The next time any of your children or your neighbors' children get sick like that, send for me immediately. Don't wait so long again." Then, when he was seated in the carriage, he bent his head to the man and said, very kindly, "I feel for your sorrow. Go to your wife. She needs you."

Béla knew how his uncle was suffering. He kept very quiet and said nothing as they drove away.

At last Dr. Telegdi burst forth. "I couldn't help her! Perhaps you should not become a doctor. Spare yourself the pain of losing a child! I was bragging today how the book of medicine was opening wide for us, but we still know so little. We have seen the diphtheria bacilli, but it doesn't behave as the anthrax does. We haven't found out how to immunize against it and it is a terrible disease. That child was strangling. The murderous bacilli make an ugly gray membrane in the throat. The muscles of the palate become paralyzed. Then death strikes at the child's heart."

He took a deep breath. "Perhaps I shouldn't fill your young mind with such horrors."

"I am going to be a doctor. I must learn about such things. It doesn't scare me." The thought flashed through Béla's mind that the only thing that frightened him was his father's fierce opposition to his becoming a doctor.

"Then you must learn, too, that in spite of all the marvelous new discoveries, we still have trouble persuading people to use them. Superstition and ignorance make patients refuse to be inoculated against smallpox. I am sure that if we find the immunity for diphtheria, they will oppose that, too," said the doctor grimly.

They slept that night in another village and returned to Boglar the next day. Every month Dr. Telegdi covered the isolated farms and villages of his three districts; even in the summer when he must also attend the fashionable and well-to-do visitors who flocked to the lake resort of Boglar.

Béla worshiped him. In a way, he felt he was almost as much his uncle's son as he was Papa Schick's. His mother had been on a visit to Boglar twelve years ago and Béla was born there —prematurely. No one thought he would live, but Dr. Telegdi had saved his life; he had given him the Hungarian name of Béla and had sworn that this child should be dedicated to saving others' lives.

Although Béla had spent his summers at Boglar, this was the first time he had been permitted to travel through the districts with his uncle. He was deeply impressed by the doctor's selfless devotion, and horrified by the agony and suffering of sick patients. The little children, helpless and wordless in their misery, stayed in his mind and could not be forgotten.

His eyes and forehead being well by the third day, he returned to Graz, where he was met at the railroad station by his father.

"You look well," he said, giving him a restrained and formal embrace. "How is your Uncle Sigismund?"

"He is fine, Papa. He took me with him on a tour of one of his districts. It was wonderful." Béla wanted to talk about it but the words died away as he saw the frown on his father's face.

"I hope you saw the farms and took note of the grain harvest this year," said his father. "No, I don't suppose you noticed that." Jacques Schick was a grain merchant. It was his firm resolve that both Richard and Béla would grow up to become partners in his business.

They walked through the beautiful Schlossberg where the clock tower was, and the ruins of the old fortress. Graz was the second largest city in Austria, only eighty miles southwest of Vienna. Béla liked to walk through it with his father. Mr. Schick was an ardent reader of history, politics and philosophy; he always had something interesting to tell.

"That cathedral," he said now, indicating a beautiful structure, "is Gothic. It was built in the medieval ages, a monument to men's sense of beauty."

"Why don't we go inside, Papa?" asked Béla.

"You may if you like, but we are Jews; the cathedral is for another religion. You might offend the worshipers because you would not know how to behave according to ritual. I am fortunate, and so are my children, that I am liked by my customers and have many friends among all kinds of people in the city. We do not suffer the persecution that other Jews do in Austria." He was being modest. He was an exceptionally popular man in the city.

"I do not understand why some people hate Jews," Béla said.

"Béla, there would be no prejudice and division between us if it weren't for ignorance and suspicion—and because our Hapsburg rulers find that prejudice pays. If the people had their way, the Hapsburgs would go; we would have a republic instead of a monarchy. They know this. So they do their best to keep us divided. They encourage the Austrians to look down on the Hungarians; the Germans in Austria to despise the Slav and the Jew. There is a slice of the Austria-Hungary nation where the people speak Italian. The Hungarians hate them."

They turned into Radetsky Street. Béla's face brightened as he caught sight of their house. "How is Mamma?" he asked.

"Waiting eagerly for you." Jacques Schick's face softened at mention of his pretty and beloved wife.

The whole family were there, waiting dinner for father and son. Janka kissed Béla, examined the place where the insect sting had been, pronounced him well, but fussed over him just the same. It was a happy and pleasant dinner. Béla's father provided a comfortable home for his family. There was a servant to help Janka, whose gentleness was the quiet hand of harmony in the household.

Yet the evening ended in an outburst of anger.

After dinner Béla's father went to his usual easy chair, with his books and papers on a convenient table, to read. Opposite him, across the table, Béla's mother cuddled the newborn Ilona for a while before she put her to bed and came back to sew. In one corner of the room Béla and Richard sat on a sofa and Béla talked of Boglar.

He was telling of the trip he had taken and without thinking, said ". . . and when I am a doctor I am going to be like Uncle Sigismund. . . ."

His father put down his newspaper and said, "I will not have such talk. You are *not* going to become a doctor! I demand that you put all such notions out of your head immediately, Béla. You are not to think of it or mention it again." He was very angry.

His wife ventured to ask, "But why, Jacques? Uncle Sigismund is successful."

"It is not necessary, my dear, that I should explain my reasons. It is sufficient that they are good reasons," he answered her.

Béla's father was a most contradictory man. His name was "Jacob" Schick, but he had changed it, not because he didn't like Jacob, but because Jacques was a French name and he was a fervent admirer of French democratic ideas. He sincerely hated tyrants, yet in his own home he considered that his word was law.

He was an intellectual. He read constantly. He wanted to give his children the best education he could afford, yet he would not allow Béla to think of going to the university. He was only a mediocre businessman and owed what success he had to his personality, rather than to any cleverness. Yet he wanted both sons to be businessmen.

In spite of this, Béla owed much to his father. He inherited from him determination and a strong character. Béla would always love books and study, just as his father did.

Béla was in his third year, of an eight-year course, at the Staats Gymnasium in Graz. Richard was one year ahead of him. It was unusual for boys of their modest circumstances to consider finishing the course; most of their classmates planned to drop out when they were about fifteen, to go to work. Only the rich or those who would go on to the university ever finished the entire eight years. Jacques Schick had promised his sons that they could graduate if they wanted to.

It was not easy. Béla would have eight years of Latin, five of Greek; he would study chemistry, biology, mathematics, geometry, history, German, French and literature. After school he took private piano lessons but Richard, who was thought to have more musical talent, went to a music school several hours a week.

This rigorous program left them with little time for play, but up until this third year in school Béla was no different from Richard or his classmates. He was a good student; not a brilliant one. He studied, but he also liked to romp with his dog or swim or fish with his brother in the river Mur, which ran beside the city close to their house.

In that third year, shortly after he had returned from his trip to Uncle Sigismund, something happened to Béla.

He had an excellent chemistry teacher, who inspired him with the desire to learn more. One day that teacher suggested that Béla might like to do some extra reading in chemistry. If so, he would find the books he wanted in the school library.

That day after school, Béla wandered into the library. He was alone at the time. He searched the shelves until he found chemistry books—but near them, on shelf after shelf, he found other books whose titles were fascinating! They were dusty books, unused, unread, just sitting there as if they had been waiting for him.

The Anatomy of the Human Body . . . *Botany: Advanced Course* . . . *The History of Medicine* . . . *The Children's Book,* by Felix Wurtz, which Béla found to be a curious book of instructions to mothers on the care of their infants.

He took them all down from the shelves and opened them on a table. He dipped into each one, tempted by a few pages here or a paragraph or a drawing there. It was almost too much. There were too many treasures and he could not decide which to read.

The next afternoon he was back in the library again. He had calmed down somewhat. The books would not run away. This time he chose the book on anatomy and began reading it from the beginning.

He was late getting home. The anatomy book had been too fascinating and the minutes had flown past. He had seen pictures of the human skeleton, with the bones and muscles all named; he had seen for himself what a marvelous and intricate thing the body is. The joints could move and bend. The neck could twist, with a complexity of the stretching and contracting of muscles. The arms could lift and carry; the hand, because of the position of the thumb, could pick things up, fashion tools, handle delicate instruments.

His mother was worried but she was not angry. Béla never saw her angry. She was concerned over his lateness and even more concerned about the strange, remote look in his eyes. He was thinking about what he had read. It was painful for him to try to put it out of his mind. Richard was waiting for him, wanting his help to build a tree house and annoyed because Béla showed no interest.

That fateful day he had put his feet onto a lonely path, where neither Richard nor his mother could follow. He must keep these precious books his own secret for the time being, but all by himself, at twelve years of age, he began the study of medicine in the school library.

2

He didn't just read the books, he studied them. He found books on hygiene, on the function of the heart, on biology. He absorbed what he read as if he were a sponge, even though he did not understand many of the technical and scientific words.

For a little while he neglected his other studies, but when his grades began to go down, he realized that would not do. His father might take him out of school. So he studied harder at home in the evenings in order to save his precious afternoon time for the library.

Jacques Schick was pleased to see Béla with his books in the evening, instead of playing games. Janka was not so sure it was a good thing: there was something unnatural in Béla's inward preoccupation. She worried. Wasn't Béla popular at school? Was he growing shy?

Richard was always full of talk of what he was doing, who his friends were, the scrapes and excitement they got into. Now the two brothers drifted slightly apart. Béla no longer had time to enter into all of Richard's plans.

Yet there was nothing Richard or his mother could complain about, because Béla seemed to have an inward happiness of his own. He was content. He was no less loving to his

27

family, always willing to help Frieda with her dolls, when their noses broke or their arms came off. He didn't mind taking care of baby Ilona. Sometimes he forgot he was a medical student and he and Richard ran, shouting and laughing, to their favorite swimming place in the river.

The years went by. Every summer Béla went to Boglar. If the rest of his family were there too, he swam in the lake with them or went on walks or enjoyed the evening band concerts. But when they left and he stayed on, he buckled down to business. He became his uncle's assistant. It was not a game. Dr. Telegdi insisted that Béla learn to help him.

He taught him the use of various instruments: the stethoscope, the tongue depresser and the injection needles. He showed him how to wrap bandages, make splints for broken arms. He allowed him into sickrooms sometimes, and showed him what symptoms to watch for in what illnesses.

He also kept him informed of the latest discoveries. The year after the insect sting incident, Dr. Telegdi told Béla in great excitement, "Do you remember the little girl who died of diphtheria? And I said we did not know how to immunize against it? My boy, a man named Emil von Behring has done it. He found that what was causing the disease was not the bacilli itself, but the poison the bacilli gave off. That poison we call toxin."

Dr. Telegdi was striding up and down his study, slapping his desk as he passed it, with a rolled-up newspaper. "So Von Behring asks himself: 'why don't all diphtheria cases die? Why do some children have light cases and recover? He found out, Béla, that the body manufactures its own defenses, called antitoxins—what does *anti* mean, Béla?"

"It means 'against' or 'opposed to,' Uncle Sigismund," he answered.

"That is right. So Von Behring reasoned that some poor children just didn't have enough antitoxins, or else the diphtheria toxin in them was so powerful their own antitoxins couldn't fight. What he did was this: he injected a horse with a weak amount of diphtheria bacilli—not enough to kill it—but enough to cause a reaction. Then he withdrew from the horse some serum. Serum is the thin, liquid part of the blood, not the red part that clots when you fall down and skin your knee. And in that serum he found lots and lots of antitoxins. Now he had *extras* to inject in a child, to help that child's own antitoxins in its battle with the toxins."

"And if a child has enough antitoxins, then they defeat the poisonous toxins and the child recovers from diphtheria!" Béla had been following step by step. "But," he said, "I wonder why it is that diphtheria only strikes at children and not at grownups."

Dr. Telegdi stopped pacing. He stared at his nephew. "I don't remember telling you that. Did I?"

Béla blushed to the roots of his dark-brown hair. He had very, very blue eyes which ordinarily looked straight at people. Now he could not look at his uncle. "I—I read it in a book. I have to tell you a secret, Uncle Sigismund. I am disobeying Papa." He told then of his library studies.

"So. What can I say?" His uncle sank down slowly into his favorite chair. "That you should not do this? That you should not disobey your father? Your Papa works hard to support you. It isn't easy for him. Your parents are fine people and they love you. Jacques Schick has a great deal of pride in you. No, I would never want you to disobey him—except in this

instance you have a greater loyalty to science—to all the suffering people."

The next year Béla went on with his reading in the library.
A fortunate thing happened. One day his favorite chemistry
professor found him reading the anatomy book after school.
Pleased, he said: "If you are very, very careful of those books,
and return them in good condition, I will give you permission
to take them home, one at a time."

"Thank you, sir." Béla was overjoyed. He had been afraid
his mother would soon be demanding an explanation of his
lateness almost every day. Now he could read at home.

When Béla was sixteen and his brother seventeen, Richard
begged his father to let him quit school and go to work. He
was bored with studying. His father pretended to scold but
he was secretly delighted to have the help of his oldest son in
his business.

It marked a real separation between the brothers. They
would defend and help and encourage each other, but Béla
was still a schoolboy while Richard thought himself a man.

Two more years went by. The great day came when Béla
graduated from the Staats Gymnasium, with fine honors. The
family celebrated in a quiet way. A few friends were invited
for supper; Dr. Telegdi was there and some of Jacques
Schick's business acquaintances. They complimented the parents on having a son with such a fine education.

"Aren't you proud of him?" they asked Janka Schick, who
placed her hand tenderly on Béla's shoulder.

"And now," they said to her husband, "what a fine thing
it will be to have him in your business. He must know a great
deal about mathematics. He can do your bookkeeping."

Béla looked up. He saw that his Uncle Sigismund was looking at him in a special, questioning way. In a little while his uncle drew him aside. "Do you want me to speak to your father tonight? The time has come, Béla, when we must insist upon your going to the university."

Béla's first inclination was to say yes. Jacques Schick would not speak harshly to Dr. Telegdi. After a moment's struggle with himself he shook his head. "No, thank you, Uncle Sigismund. I must be the one who talks to him. I must prove to him that I am not a child."

He caught the seven-year-old Frieda up into his arms as she came running to him.

"I am going to school, too!" she boasted. "Will they have a party for me when I graduate, Béla?"

"Of course they will," he answered. "A *big* party."

"You still have a way with children, don't you, Béla," Dr. Telegdi commented. "That is an excellent thing."

Béla made up his mind to speak to his father the very next day. Now that the guests were gone and the supper cleared away, the children were tired from all the excitement, and were sent to bed.

In his own room, Béla could not think of sleep. He did not undress. He opened the window wide and sat on the sill, looking out over the shadowed buildings of the little city. Here and there the gas lamps were lit on street corners; candlelight glowed softly from windows; church bells were ringing faintly in the distance.

Graz was beautiful. There was much for a young man to enjoy in it. Richard went to parties, invited his friends to the coffee shops, enjoyed boating trips on the river in the summer or went hiking in the mountains. All that took money, but he had a salary. If Béla went to the university—if he could persuade his father to let him go—there would be no parties, no friendships or courtships for him. There would only be work, but it was what he wanted. Suddenly he got to his feet. Why put it off until tomorrow? He would not be less afraid tomorrow!

He went back into the living room where his father read under one lamp and his mother sewed under another, with the table between them. It was a familiar picture. For a second Béla hesitated, hating to break up the peace and harmony.

His mother looked up. "Can you not sleep, Béla? Are you restless?"

"I must speak to Papa. I must—" Béla plunged in desperately, anxious to get it over.

"Then speak." The newspaper rustled but Jacques Schick did not remove it from in front of his face. "I know what you are going to say. Your uncle leaves me no peace. He talks of nothing else, since you were born. You want to be a doctor."

"Yes, please, Papa. I know it is asking a lot of you, after the expense of the Gymnasium, but all I need is my tuition and the cost of books. I will not ask for another groschen from you," pleaded Béla.

"You must think I am a rich man, to send a son to the university." The newspaper went down and Papa Schick glared at Béla. "I am not rich. I have already done more for you than most fathers. Soon Frieda will have to have money to go to the Lyceum; then there will be Ilona. Must I support you in idleness?" He stopped. He was a fair and just man. "No, that is not so. You would not be idle. You would study, I know. But I do not believe that you would be content at the university in shabby clothes, without money in your pockets to entertain your classmates."

Béla demolished the argument. "I have no interest in theaters or coffee shops. All I want is the chance to be a doctor. If you can't afford it, Papa, I'll work somewhere nights for my tuition. I'll wash dishes in a café. I'll be a night watchman. I'll do anything."

Both Mr. and Mrs. Schick stared at him, startled by his passion and by the grown-up determination in his voice. For the first time it was evident that Béla was no longer a boy, to be made to obey.

Jacques Schick's voice was more reasoning than severe, when he spoke again. "Sit down, Béla, and let us talk about this. I wanted to be a doctor, once. I studied in Hungary. The courses are impossibly rigorous. Those who passed had the money to pay for tutors and coaches—"

"All your courses were taught in Latin, Papa," Béla interrupted. "That is not true at the Karl Franz University in Graz." It was also on the tip of his tongue to say that Uncle Sigismund had passed the Hungarian exams without money for special coaching, but he had the sense not to say it and anger his father still more. "Besides, I have a good start in medical learning."

"Because your uncle has let you 'play' at being his assistant? Nonsense!" said his father.

"No, because I have been reading and studying medical books for the past six years. I know they are old-fashioned books and out-of-date; I found them in the school library. Just the same, I have learned a great deal from them."

"I am astonished. You have been doing this and I did not know of it? Béla, you are either the most obstinate or the most disobedient boy—I don't know what to think." He leaned forward and touched Béla's knee. "Listen to me. I could scrape up the money for your tuition. I know you would study hard and probably graduate well. But what then? You are a Jew. If you are to succeed as a doctor you must acquire a rich and influential practice. It is precisely the rich and influential who look with contempt at Jews and affect to despise us. Don't tell me that Dr. Telegdi has such a practice. He does, but it was accidental that he settled in Boglar; accidental that there was no other doctor nearby for the wealthy vacationers; accidental that he is a genius . . . which, proud though I am of my sons, I do not believe you are."

Having got off this long-winded oration, the matter was ended, or so Papa Schick seemed to think, as he settled back in his chair and took up his newspaper.

Béla thought otherwise. He said quietly, "I am going to be a doctor, Papa, whether you help me or not."

His father raised his hand and slapped it hard against the arm of his chair. He exploded. "Then do so! Leave me in peace. Yes, I will give you your tuition and money for your books—but not a penny more!"

His wife knew how to soothe his injured feelings. While Béla sat, dazed at the sudden capitulation, she said, "That is a fine and generous thing to do, Jacques. Béla will always be grateful to you and work hard and bring credit to us." She made a tiny signal with her hand for Béla to leave them.

"Thank you, Papa. I—I—thank you so much," Béla stammered, getting out of the room as fast as he could.

Alone in his room he felt as if a miracle had happened. He could not believe it. He was going to the university. He would be enrolled as a medical student. He would become a doctor.

Usually Béla Schick's face was restrained, thoughtful, quiet, lightened sometimes by a shy smile of amusement. Tonight it was glowing and alive. His blue eyes blazed with happiness. A thin, dark, medium-sized young man, apt to pass unnoticed in a crowd, tonight he felt a giant. He wanted to laugh, to sing. He had to talk to someone. He went into Richard's room and sat on the edge of his bed and woke him up.

"Richard, I am going to the university. Papa just said so."

Richard rubbed his eyes. Sorrowfully, he said, "Are they *making* you go?"

Then Béla did laugh. "Making me? Papa couldn't stop me."

That fall of 1895 he enrolled at the Karl Franz University, in the very small medical department. There were only thirty students and several professors. It was a small school but a good one. The professors were young; several of them already had nationwide reputations.

The rest of the university ignored the medical students, unless they met them in the hallways. Then they held their noses. At that time the antiseptic used in the medical clinics was a preparation called udiform and it stank to the heavens. The medical students were proud of it; they wore their awful stench as a proud banner of their chosen profession.

In the first few months Béla's father repeatedly asked him if the lessons were not too hard; if he did not mind being out of the gay and roisterous side of university life; if he would not rather quit and go into the grain business. After a while he stopped asking. Béla always looked as if the questions were madness. He set out each morning for his classes, with a blithe eagerness which utterly dumfounded both his father and his brother.

They could not know the dynamic mental activity which seethed through the medical department, in fact, through all the medical schools of Europe at that time.

Dr. Telegdi had been right. This was the age when the medical Book of Knowledge was just opening up. Once Louis Pasteur had shown that it was bacteria which caused so many serious illnesses, other great men had followed with new discoveries. In 1880, Karl Joseph Eberth discovered the cause of typhoid fever—the typhoid bacillus; in 1882, Robert Koch discovered the tubercle bacillus and, in 1883, his assistant Fehleisen proved that erysipelas was caused by a streptococcus, a form of bacteria. Also in that year Koch isolated the bacteria of cholera. There was excitement in every school and laboratory. Medical journals multiplied in number, to keep up with the tremendous leaps in medical science.

There were several forms of bacteria. A bacillus was one; a streptococcus was another. In 1885 a very young man by the name of Theodor Escherich found the bacillus coli, in the intestinal canal. In 1894, a Frenchman, Alexandre Émile Jean Yersin, discovered the bacillus which caused bubonic plague —at the very same time that a Japanese named Shibasaburo Kitazato did the identical thing, in Japan.

No wonder the students of the Karl Franz University thought of nothing but bacteriology. Its message drummed in their blood. They, too, would make discoveries and be famous.

They were awed by the fact that one of those gods of bacteriology, young Theodor Escherich, had recently come to Graz and was teaching in their own university. But most of the students were ashamed that such a brilliant man should be teaching pediatrics.

What was *pediatrics?* Who ever heard of it? It was supposed to deal with children and children's diseases, but the students knew that other doctors laughed at the idea. It was all foolish nonsense and an idle fad to think that children needed a special doctor.

As a freshman student, Béla was not yet studying either bacteriology or pediatrics. He had anatomy and physiology and pathology. He was learning about the human body in health and in disease. His class was even taken to the autopsy room. He didn't mind touching dead bodies, though he had been afraid he would, because he could learn from them how to save live patients.

He wrote about this to his uncle, who answered him with a family secret. "Don't tell your father that I am giving away something he is ashamed of," Dr. Telegdi wrote, "but he couldn't stand the autopsy room when he was a medical student. He used to take a big bite of an apple before going in, and keep it in his mouth and bite hard on it when he had to operate on a dead body. It didn't help him. He was nauseated every time." Reading the letter, Béla could hear his uncle chuckling as he wrote this. "I'm proud of you," the letter continued. "You are developing the true, scientific detachment that a medical researcher must have."

While his uncle would always and forever have a cherished niche in Béla's heart, he was gaining new idols.

Professor Escherich was one, but as yet Béla had no courses with him. The man with whom he came into immediate contact was Professor Friedrich Kraus, the inspired teacher of bacteriology, physiology, biology, and the innovator of the demonstration clinic at the university. His lectures were brilliant; never to be forgotten. He spoke to his students on the role of a doctor.

"A physician or a surgeon must be a selfless individual. He holds the lives and health of people in his two hands; he must hold them also in his brain and in his heart. Never let me hear you young gentlemen say that you are treating a leg or an arm of a patient." He had compassion for humanity, did Professor Kraus, but none for his students. He was sternly ruthless with them. "Remember, you are treating a whole person."

Béla was seated in the front row, taking notes. He listened intently.

"Some of you," Professor Kraus went on, "will become general physicians, handling every kind of ailment, even minor surgery. Others may specialize in obstetrics or may wish to teach part of the day in a university and have a private practice on the side. Whatever you do, it must not be for money or reputation. It must be to help humanity."

The student sitting next to Béla made an involuntary, quick movement, as if in protest. Béla glanced at him and saw him frown, then bend his head to hide his face from Professor Kraus's penetrating glance.

After class that same student talked to Béla and several others, as they made their way down the hall to another classroom. "I give Kraus credit," he said loftily, "for being a fine teacher, but his ideals are unrealistic. I intend to have a good income from my practice. There's no money in teaching or research. What we have to do is study the situation in some good-sized town or city and go into partnership with some doctor who is already established. What you have to guard against is getting stuck in some village where the peasants pay you in potatoes." Some of the other students laughed at this. Béla didn't, nor did one other—a tall, thin student named Clemens von Pirquet.

"Why," asked Béla, stung out of his shyness by the crude

money hunger of the one who had spoken, "did you ever want to become a doctor? If it is money you want, be a businessman. How can you take care of a patient's illness, if all you are thinking about is your pocketbook?"

"Don't pretend to me that you'd just as soon starve as be rich!" countered the other angrily. "Don't pretend that you'd just as soon go to a workman's hut as to a count's mansion, if you had to make a choice between those two patients."

Clemens von Pirquet spoke before Béla could frame a reply. "He would," he said, meaning Béla. "Professor Kraus would. I would. It's a good thing for medicine and for all suffering people, my friend, that you find your moneygrubbing ideas are in the minority here." His words were tinged with such a natural arrogance, and his manner was so lofty that the student was squelched and said no more.

Béla Schick and Clemens von Pirquet looked at each other. A smile of understanding passed between them.

The first year ended, but Béla had had to work hard and study long, long hours. He had done very well, and his father had stopped questioning him. There was no doubt that Béla was determined to complete the four years.

Though his interests and his medical studies made a sharp separation between him and his family, nothing could change the deep affection they had for him, and he for them. His father tried to hide his feelings. He was stern; he was often unjust to Béla, but he could not conceal entirely the pride in this intelligent son.

Béla had no time for any real social life. He made a few friends at the university—students with whom he walked a few blocks in the mornings, or when he left his classes in the evenings.

There was one student he wanted to know. He would have liked to be friends with Clemens von Pirquet, because they seemed to share a special attitude toward their classes. Neither of them lounged in the hallways, gossiping. Neither of them ever came late to classes, or gave excuses for not coming at all. Von Pirquet's dark eyes were alive with vitality; his face was thin with the inward drive which pushed him almost beyond his physical strength.

It wasn't likely that they would be friends. They came to the university from entirely different worlds.

Béla watched Clemens von Pirquet stride from the autopsy room one day, with his hurried, long-legged walk.

"What do you suppose is driving him?" One student asked another. Béla overheard; he was putting away some of the instruments used by the students. The professor trusted few people to handle these correctly, but he trusted Béla Schick.

"I don't know," said the other. "He doesn't have to work. He comes from Hirschstetten and his family is an old and wealthy line of landowners there. He even has the aristocratic "von" title in front of his name. He was sent to the finest preliminary schools; his mother was determined he should be a priest. He spent three years in a theological academy and then he suddenly left it and said he was going to become a doctor. Maybe he's pushing and driving himself to make up for three years of the time he wasn't studying medicine—he is older than most of us."

"I heard Professor Kraus say he is brilliant." The first student wiped his hands on a towel, carelessly tossed it onto a table. He left the autopsy room with his friend, remarking as he did, "I wish I had his money and his title and brains. I wouldn't be slaving away as a medical student, believe me."

What Béla had overheard put more distance between them. Von Pirquet had a title and wealth; he was brilliant. Béla did not have one cent in his pocket nor a title to his name. He did not think of himself as particularly talented—though his teachers frequently complimented him.

When he was twenty-one, he began his third year of medical studies. His future seemed to lie plain and straight before him. When he graduated next year he would go into practice with his uncle.

In that third year at the university, Béla began the study of bacteriology. He found that this research fascinated him. He had a natural equipment for it; he was a careful, cautious, painstaking worker, and his curiosity was insatiable, allowing him to take absolutely nothing for granted.

The very first day, when Béla was one of ten students assigned to the small room fitted up as a laboratory, his eyes roamed with eagerness over the tables with their burden of odd-looking tubes and flasks, bottles with long, thin necks, and glass jars. His hands itched to handle the microscopes. There were only two of them for all the students.

Professor Kraus gave a brief lecture first. "You will be examining in this room bacteria which are harmless and those which are deadly. The harmless ones can be found in soil and milk and sugars and waters. The deadly ones will be in cultures or serums. I am speaking of their danger to the patient; they are dangerous to you, too, but that is unimportant."

Someone stifled a nervous laugh. Professor Kraus frowned,

then went on sarcastically. "You must learn a profound respect for these little forms of life which you cannot see without a microscope. If you learn proper methods of handling them on slides or preparing them in cultures, you will be perfectly safe. If you do not," he shrugged, "well, you probably wouldn't have made a good doctor anyway and will be no loss to mankind."

Two of the students were ordered to sit on stools in front of the microscopes. Professor Kraus instructed them to remove the bell jar which kept the instruments free of dust. "Now place the eyepiece into the tube carefully. Adjust the position of the mirror so that the proper illumination is obtained. If you have too much light and glare, move the microscope." He watched their fumbling hands and shook his head disdainfully. "You are not driving a horse and wagon! These are delicate instruments. Herr Schick and—yes, Herr von Pirquet—will you two take their places? I believe you can help me demonstrate without breakage."

Béla sat in front of one microscope; across the table at another sat Von Pirquet. Both had slim fingers. Both touched their microscopes with a firm but light touch as they adjusted the eyepieces to their satisfaction.

"Now," continued the professor, "take these slides and place them under the spring clips and move them so that the object in the center of the slides comes as nearly in the center of your focus as possible."

Béla stared through the eyepiece, while he moved the slide gently back and forth. For a second he was ashamed of himself. He could see only a blur. What was he doing that was wrong? He could feel sweat coming out on his forehead. It would be awful to be disgraced in front of the class.

He changed the focus. Suddenly the clear picture leaped up at him. He gasped out loud. Almost at the same time he heard a mutter of satisfaction from across the table.

"What do you see, Herr Schick?" asked Professor Kraus.

"Long, slender objects, like thin rods," reported Béla, keeping his eyes glued to the microscope. His hands were trembling but from nervous excitement. "They don't seem to be moving."

"Move the slide a little," ordered the professor.

"Now they are drifting," Béla said as he moved the slide. "I thought they were all straight but I see one which is slightly curved—"

"Is each rod alone or in groups?"

Here Béla almost made a mistake. His eyes were becoming strained by the tension of his task. "I would say they are alone —no, wait; there are some in pairs."

"Herr von Pirquet?" snapped out the professor.

"I see the same," Clemens von Pirquet answered. "I thought they were single at first but there are many that seem to be in pairs. Herr Schick saw some that were curved. I have found one which seems to be in the shape of a club, but most are those slender rods."

"Very good. Very good, indeed. I am delighted with both of you for your excellent powers of observation. What you are seeing and handling, gentlemen, is the virulent, deadly diphtheria bacilli. Aren't you frightened? No? That is good. Actually, the culture in which those bacilli are suspended is in a slight concavity in the slide and there is a cover slip over them, so the danger is not as great as you might fear."

Béla felt no fear. His mind had flashed to a small child

named Sophie. So these innocent-looking little things were the cause of the terrible gray stuff in a child's throat which could strangle her! He felt divided in his feelings—rage against the murdering bacillus for what it did to a child, and scientific detachment which knew that the bacillus had no mind or will of its own, knew nothing of what it was doing, but was compelled by its nature to do it.

Professor Kraus ordered two more students to the microscopes. Béla let go of his reluctantly, and stepped back into the group. As he did so he found himself side by side with Clemens von Pirquet.

Again the two exchanged an involuntary smile which said plainly that they had enjoyed sharing a tremendous experience together.

"All bacteria," the professor told them as he carefully watched the students at the table, "—and bacilli are just one form of bacteria—have certain things in common. Some are round, some are long and slender. Some bring on one disease and some another. But they are all small. They are composed of just one cell. They are alive. They breathe. They reproduce themselves. They must have nourishment. They eventually die. Where do they live? Almost everywhere. In the soil, in water, carried by the dust through the air or exhaled by our breath. They are constantly on the surface of our bodies, but only if they can get into the body, in sufficient numbers, in vulnerable spots, can they do damage."

"But if they are on our bodies and getting into our throats, why aren't more of us ill from them?" asked one student.

"Think of them as an army invading the body. The body can raise its own army, in defense. If the body fights and conquers, then the body is immune to the next attack of that same bacteria." Professor Kraus was intensely serious. "Think of yourselves, gentlemen, as the Intelligence Corps of the body's defense. You will be captains in that corps; be proud if you choose that service."

3

Be proud if you choose that service! The words lingered on in Béla's mind. It was a service he thought he would like to choose. He felt he was suited for it.

He did not scorn the general practice of Dr. Telegdi, but there was no laboratory at Boglar. He remembered well the unselfish service of his uncle and how people loved him. This could be his own life in Boglar, but he was beginning to feel strongly, urgently, that his place was in a hospital which had a laboratory for research.

At the same time he did not want *just* the laboratory. One of his friends in his class did, since he had little interest in the human patient. It was the explorations inside the laboratory which interested him.

Béla could not be like that. The laboratory was a means to an end, and that end was the healing of men, women and, particularly, children. He never lost sight of the ailing figure on a sickbed.

Professor Kraus tried to keep this image always in the minds of his students. In addition to their laboratory work, he gave demonstration clinics where patients from the university hospital were brought into a small room, so that the students

could watch as he diagnosed symptoms and discussed treatment.

One cold and snowy day in December, Béla hurried up the steps of the medical school, stamping his feet on each stone step to get the caked ice off his shoes. He shivered as he took off his thin jacket and pushed back his wet, dark hair. He hurried down the corridor. Turning into the doorway of the demonstration room, he breathed a sigh of relief. He wasn't late. Professor Kraus, his assistant and the patient were still to come. Béla nodded to the others and spoke to a few he knew well.

"Why does Professor Kraus worry you so much?" he asked one friend who was visibly nervous. "He snaps, but he doesn't bite."

"All very well for you to say," grumbled the other, "when you know all the answers and he likes you."

"Likes me? He hardly knows I exist." Béla scoffed.

Just then Professor Kraus entered, followed by another half-dozen students. An attendant wheeled in a bed on which lay a hospital patient.

Without wasting any time, the Professor began. "Herr Schick, will you act as my assistant today? Mine is working on a special article and I do not wish to take him away from it." Surprised but pleased, Béla took his position beside the teacher who went on speaking. "Today I am going to ask Herr Schick to make a complete diagnosis, without preparation, of this man's condition. The rest of you are free to question him, criticize his diagnosis or offer your own. Proceed, Herr Schick."

Béla felt cold tremors run along his spine, but he tried to convince himself it was only the temperature of the room. He knew in his heart he was frightened at making a bad mistake. He took his time. He first examined the patient's eyes, face and throat, speaking to him gently and saying, "Do you mind, sir, if I turn your chin a little?" Then he pulled down the sheet and with all of his acquired knowledge, his brain, his eyes, the touch of his hands—yes, even his nose, sniffing for certain characteristic odors of disease—he made the diagnosis.

"The patient," he said, "is a man of approximately forty years, of slight frame; his hands show no evidence of manual labor. He wears eyeglasses, though he is not wearing them now. He has had smallpox as a child. There are a few smallpox marks still visible on the left side of his chin. Even without turning him over I think there is a light curvature of the spine, probably due to faulty posture. If this patient were a book-keeper, habitually crouched over his desk, that might account for it."

Béla took a deep breath. Thus far it had not been difficult. Now he had to state why this man was bedridden.

"He is suffering from a small growth, a tumor, of the groin. By palpitation I could feel the mass, though it is not visible on the surface."

"Are you certain?" asked Professor Kraus, in a forbidding way.

"Of the tumor, yes sir, I am. Of the curvature of the spine, no—that is a guess, and I could not be sure unless I could examine the spine." Béla answered.

"Nevertheless you are quite correct. It was a good guess. I might add that Herr Jodel is a bookkeeper, so you were right about that, although I don't like my students pulling rabbits out of hats and thinking they are magicians. Your diagnosis of

the tumor was a splendid one. I would not have been surprised if you had missed it."

As Béla stepped aside so that Professor Kraus could lecture on both the symptoms and the treatment, he felt a glow, knowing his teacher thought well of him.

When the lecture was over he had another nice surprise. Clemens von Pirquet followed him out and said, "That was good work you did in the diagnosis, Herr Schick."

"Thank you, Herr von Pirquet."

"Please—I dislike titles," said the other. "Will you just call me Pirquet? Or better still, just Clemens?"

"I will." Béla held out his hand. "My name is Béla." He added, with a touch of humor, "We'll both be doctors in another year. You won't mind that title, will you?"

"That's the only one I'd be proud of!" Clemens answered.

This morning set its seal on their liking for each other. If they had had time and not been so driven by their work, if they had lived near each other or ever had occasion to walk together in the same direction, they might have become friends. As it was they had time only for a few moments of talk before or after a class.

In Béla's fourth year another bond was forged between them. They were among the few students who chose to take classes in pediatrics from Professor Escherich. Clemens Pirquet had said, openly, that he was going to do postgraduate study in pediatrics.

"You may not think it of much importance now, as a special branch of medicine, but I believe that someday only pediatricians will be called in to treat children. There will be special research into the diseases of children, and even special hospitals," he said, arguing with a group of students in the hospital library one day.

Most of the students were a little in awe of Clemens von Pirquet's ancestry, his name and wealth, his brilliance and the fact that he was slightly older, but this statement of his was too much for them to take without laughter. "You don't really mean that!" scoffed one. "What is pediatrics anyway? Why do you need special physicians and surgeons for children? The structure of their bodies is no different from that of adults, except for size. If you understand the nervous system and the insides of one, you know them for both child and adult."

"That is not true," said Béla. "Children are not small adults. They have diseases which adults do not. They have special problems because of their rapid growth. They need special foods, particularly the very young ones."

"Nonsense. Any good doctor can do the job just as well as your fancy pediatrician. I can't understand two men, as smart as you and Béla, wanting to go into such a field. Why don't you set yourselves up in an office and get a wealthy practice? Or if you want to stick to research, why not concentrate on bacteriology?"

"I intend to use my interest in bacteriology to explore the infectious diseases of children," answered Clemens von Pirquet.

Béla felt a real wrench at his heart. How gladly he would have shouted the same thing, if he had the right. But did he? His father had provided tuition and money for books, against his will, true, but he had done it, nevertheless. How could his son tell him that he was going to desert the financial secur-

ity he would have in Boglar, to go into a little-known, hardly recognized branch of medicine called pediatrics?

And if he did go in for pediatrics, he would have to work as an unpaid volunteer under Professor Escherich to get the necessary experience.

Yet that day, when Professor Escherich escorted his few pupils over to the small Children's Clinic, Béla knew he wanted that unpaid job more than anything in the world. Looking at all those children, he could almost *feel* what they were thinking—what they wanted—where they hurt and ached—

He pulled his thoughts back to the professor, who was speaking.

"Pediatrics, gentlemen," he was saying, "has a future so important that we can only dare now to imagine it. You, who voluntarily attend me here in the clinic and come to my lectures, must have some imagination, but most of the medical world does not." He spoke gravely.

Tall, erect, impressive in manner and in appearance, he awed his students. Though not yet middle-aged, he was a serious man. He rarely smiled. His eyes were frosty, remote, but could be suddenly penetrating and keen. He cultivated a full beard, which added to his years. Béla thought he was the very opposite of Professor Kraus, who bounced from sarcasm to praise, from anger to laughter.

Now Professor Escherich paused in the ward aisle and looked at each student in turn. "Why are you here? To gain a little insight into children's diseases, to help you in your general practice? That is good but it is not enough. I am hoping that some of you will dedicate your lives to pediatrics."

He went up to a cot and bent over a three-year-old, saying

at the same time, "The small child is not just a small adult, but an entity in himself, with special problems of growth and development, immunities, diseases and susceptibilities. Bone and muscle and tissues are growing and changing. We must learn—and then teach the world—the proper food to build these small bodies, to protect these small bodies—" he carefully lifted the child into his arms "—and to understand these little minds."

He talked to the child now. "The world has not treated you well, has it, little one?" He was not smiling but somehow the child knew she was in friendly hands; she relaxed. "Your parents loved you but they had seven others; they did not know that you needed a special diet because your stomach could not digest the cabbage and potatoes the others ate. When you vomited they called you a 'naughty girl.' No, no!" he said to the child who was shrinking back in his arms. "You are a good girl, a very good, sweet girl. You will go back to bed now and rest and have the special diet and be all well soon."

After he had placed her back on her pillow, Professor Escherich led the way to the next bed, speaking in low tones to his students. "Try not to discuss, as I did just then, a child's case in front of her. Children understand more than you think; on the other hand, a careless word can cause them unnecessary worry. That little girl was so frightened at home that she stopped talking; almost stopped walking. She was reverting to being a baby, in face of pain and punishment she didn't understand. Now she talks a little."

As it had on that memorable day when he had accompanied his uncle on his district tour, it was the helplessness of this little girl, and all children, which pulled so strongly at Béla's deepest sympathies. He wanted so much to help them. He knew he could, if he only had the chance.

When they finished checking all the children and left the ward, the professor gathered his students around him in a small group. "Never pretend to a child that nothing is wrong with him; he knows there is. He must learn to trust you and your word. Here in these wards I am changing old procedures. Some of the nurses find it difficult to change. I impress upon them that a child seldom can give an accurate picture to an adult of what is wrong with him. Even less can he understand why we do the things we do—stick him with needles, give him purges, deny him candy, keep him in bed when he wants to run and play. To be a pediatrician takes infinite patience, carefulness, gentleness, firmness. And love, gentlemen. Those children in there respond to love when all the pills fail.

"Today," Professor Escherich finished his lecture, "there are only a handful of pediatricians in the world. This university and the University of Vienna are two of the pioneers in creating a Pediatrics Department. I believe that someday there will be thousands of pediatricians; every large university will have its Pediatric Department; there will be pediatric wards in every large hospital—perhaps special hospitals just for children."

As Béla went home he was thinking of some of the things Professor Escherich had said, and this led, inevitably, to the worry over his own situation. It occurred to him: if he valued his mother's love so much, why didn't he worry about her reaction to his new dreams? Why was he always thinking of his father?

The answer was, he realized, that his mother had no personal ambitions for him. She wanted him to be happy. Oh, she was anxious for his future, but not in the same way his father was.

"Don't you want to get married?" she asked him that afternoon, as he sat in front of the blue-and-white tiled stove in the dining room, a book in his hand, while she set the table for dinner. "Serena is married and already has a daughter. Her little Erna adores you. Don't you want children of your own? Look at Richard; he's already courting two pretty girls."

"When I am in the Children's Hospital, Mamma," Béla said, "all those children are mine."

Janka Schick shook her blond head. She did not understand.

"Leave him alone." Jacques Schick had come in, unnoticed. "When he goes to Boglar and is established in practice there, he'll have plenty of time to look for a wife. But you'd better hurry up, Béla, because I think your Uncle Sigismund is planning to get married himself, and he'll probably take the prettiest woman in Boglar."

Béla's heart sank. His father was looking forward to that day when his son would be his uncle's assistant. Béla looked at the father and saw a new streak of gray in his hair and lines in his face. The grain business was having a bad year. Frieda was now at the expensive Lyceum school. Ilona would be going there in a couple of years.

How could he ask more of his father? How could he destroy those cheerful hopes?

He couldn't. He resolved to give up all those wonderful dreams of becoming a volunteer worker in the Pediatrics Department.

Near the end of the year Béla presented himself for his examinations. They were handled in this way: when a last-year student felt himself ready to graduate, he sent formal, engraved notices to his professors, then dressed in his best clothes and presented himself to the professor in his office or home and there took an oral examination in that particular course.

The procedure terrified the students. Because there were only thirty of them, the professors knew them well, understood their weaknesses or suspected what they had not memorized. At that time Austria-Hungary, Germany and France were competing for the finest medical reputation in the world. Standards were high. Unless a student was really good, he did not pass.

Clemens von Pirquet had already gone through this ordeal and passed with highest honors.

Béla did not know what to expect. He had no very good opinion of himself, yet he knew he had worked and studied harder than most of his classmates.

In the first new suit he had had in four years, Béla presented himself first to Professor Kraus. He sat stiffly on the edge of a chair as the teacher looked over the pile of reports on his desk. "Ah, yes," said the professor, glancing at one page, "I seem to remember you made a mistake one day in class on the diseases primarily of bovine origin. Name for me those diseases which are transmitted through milk."

"Tuberculosis," answered Béla promptly, trying to swallow with a dry throat. "Mastitis; undulant fever or contagious abortion; foot-and-mouth disease; cowpox and anthrax."

"Correct. And what is serum?" the professor shot at him quickly.

"Serum?" This was almost too easy. "Serum is the straw-colored liquid which separates the clotting of blood from the clot and the corpuscles. It is the more fluid constituent of blood or lymph or milk or similar animal liquids. Within the serum are many types of protective substances and—"

"Enough." Professor Kraus put aside papers and records, turned his chair to face Béla more squarely, and smiled at him. "For the sake of university regulations, I had to ask you some questions, but they were not necessary. I know your record, Herr Schick. You are one of the most outstanding students I have ever had. I have no hesitation in saying that you have special qualities of obstinate determination and thoughtful, intelligent, careful attention to work, combined with a curiosity that takes nothing for granted. I hope that you have made up your mind to become a bacteriologist?"

Béla plunged from the heights of joy, at the compliments, to the depth of despair. He bent his head and twisted his new hat round and round between his fingers. "No, I am sorry, Professor Kraus. I must obey my family's wishes and go into practice with my uncle."

"The duty to your family is important," said Professor Kraus, looking upset and disappointed. "Well, then, there is nothing more to say, except to congratulate you on your splendid showing at the Karl Franz University."

Béla's next appointment that day was with Professor Escherich. The head of pediatrics did not waste time asking any questions—except one. "What do you intend to do with your future? Surely you realize that you must do postgraduate work. With your brain, Herr Schick, you cannot be satisfied with what you have learned so far; you are equipped now to make a simple diagnosis and feed pills to patients. Have you thought of going in for pediatrics? Of all my pupils, you and Dr. von Pirquet most interest me."

Words, pent up, came out of Béla in a rush. "There is

nothing I should like to do more, Herr Professor, but I cannot. I have always, always, wanted to be a physician; I know now that I have always wanted to be a children's physician. There are reasons why I cannot." He explained about his father and his uncle's offer to make him an assistant.

"It is a great pity," was Professor Escherich's comment. "For the sake of the children who need you, I would almost call it a tragedy. However, if you cannot work under me, perhaps you can arrange to come up from time to time for my lectures. Dr. von Pirquet will begin as one volunteer in the Pediatrics Department this fall."

Béla again said how sorry he was, and took his leave. The rest of his interviews were easy. He was graduated with the highest marks. He was now entitled to call himself Dr. Schick.

This great moment in his life found him miserable, but pretending contentment to please his mother and father. They were overjoyed. Richard bragged about his brilliant brother. Frieda acted toward him with great dignity, since she was now a young lady of thirteen and he was twenty-three. Ilona tried her best to copy Frieda but giggled every time she said "Doctor."

Uncle Sigismund, who had now married, expected Béla to come immediately to Boglar and become his assistant and part of his household, but Béla had a sudden reprieve. He was informed that he had to perform his military service, required of all young men in Austria-Hungary.

Since that would happen in a few months Béla persuaded his father and uncle that it would not be wise for him to go to Boglar and start practice, only to have to break it off. Instead, he would attend special lectures that summer at the university

and do volunteer work for Professor Kraus. It was too late to
work under Professor Escherich—that place had been filled.

Professor Kraus was delighted to have him. Béla was not
paid, of course, since it was customary for young men to fill out
a term as unsalaried volunteers before becoming *Sekundars,*
then assistants, and finally working up to full professorships.
His work with Professor Kraus that summer was only part
time, which left him free to spend as many hours as he could
squeeze out at the Children's Clinic.

He was feeling the joy of reprieve when it was snatched
away from him. Uncle Sigismund, never suspecting that Béla
was not anxious to work in Boglar, wrote to ask if he would
fill in for a month that summer, while he and his new wife
took a vacation. Béla had no choice. He apologized to Professor Kraus, who said he fully understood. He also promised
Béla a place in the University Hospital and laboratory any
time he wished to come back.

In Boglar, after his uncle and his new aunt left, he controlled
his temper with rich vacationers who wanted to talk for hours
about their aches and pains and mosquito bites. They liked
him. He seemed a nice, modest, very intelligent physician, who
would soon be a credit to his uncle. It was different when he
went on the district rounds to the villages. The farmers were
suspicious of him. He was too young. He was not Dr. Telegdi,
in whom they had an almost superstitous faith that he could
cure anything that was wrong with them.

It is a good life, Béla repeated to himself, over and over.
*They will learn to trust me. I can settle down and make the
best of it.*

The effort to forget the laboratory, the hospital, the Children's Clinic, wore on his nerves. Small things made him

discouraged. One day he examined a man who had an infection of his mouth which did not respond to any treatment. "You should go immediately to Budapest and have the hospital treat this," he recommended. But the man refused. "Thank you, Dr. Schick, but I will wait for Dr. Telegdi. He will know what to do."

It was a relief when his uncle returned and Béla set out, in the uniform of a medical captain, for the fortress of Komarno on the Danube River, to do his military service.

Once there, he found he had almost nothing to do. It was peace time. There were only minor illnesses, or cuts or bruises, to attend to. For the first time since he had been a child he had long days of idleness and lots of time to think. It was a strange interval in his life.

There was an excellent piano in the officer's quarters and Béla had not forgotten his music lessons. He played his favorite concertos and found they released the worry from his mind. They helped to clear away confusion. In the grandeur of music he felt the grandeur of man.

He came to see that the single life of a man was not his to waste or throw away. He, Dr. Béla Schick, owed a duty to mankind. He owed a duty to his father, too, but not to the extent of burying his real talents in Boglar or twisting out of shape the real purpose of his life.

He came to a decision. It would have to be a compromise. Not even good, generous, understanding Uncle Sigismund would stand by him if he chose pediatrics; physicians thought pediatrics a ridiculous fad. Uncle Sigismund would understand, as one doctor to another, Béla's preference for research in bacteriology. Béla could refuse to go to Boglar but he

would have to work for Professor Kraus, even if Professor
Escherich had room for him as a volunteer.

At least he would be studying and learning; he would
be in a large hospital, with a laboratory to work in. With this
decision came a release and a great sense of happiness. He went
for long walks in the beautiful, wooded countryside. He made
a few friends. When he played music, his fingers began to
improvise happy, quick-step tunes.

The regiment had an excellent band. Béla had fun compos-
ing new marches for them. To his great amazement the band
conductor liked them so much he incorporated them into the
regiment's regular parade music. Even more surprising, those
same marches of Béla Schick's found their way to other regi-
ments and finally became part of the regular army music all
over the Empire!

He was not thinking of music, however, when his service
was over and he came home to Graz. The family saw immediately the change in him. He had matured. The small army
mustache he had cultivated was becoming to him; it made him
look older, but the real maturity showed in the steadiness of
his blue eyes.

He spoke to his father the very first day. He explained,
firmly, why he could not become his uncle's assistant and why
he intended working under Professor Kraus.

"I'm not surprised," his father grumbled. "You don't do
anything the way other people do. Always you must be different. You couldn't even be *born* at the same time other
children are; you had to come early!" He crossed his arms and
glared at his son. "What will your uncle think? He has
counted on you. All right, all right—I am as foolish as you

are. If you must do this I will see you have a place to sleep in my house and food to eat."

Dr. Telegdi was hurt, too, but he was understanding. If bacteriology was Béla's star, then he must follow it.

The welcome back which he got from Professor Kraus was flattering. Béla became his assistant, though he didn't have the title. He also had time to visit the Children's Clinic.

Nothing pleased him so much as his reception there by Clemens von Pirquet. "This is splendid!" he exclaimed. "I have wished so often that you were a volunteer here, with me, and the two of us could work together and talk things over together. Even if you don't have much time for us, we shall make every moment count."

"I look forward to it," replied Béla. He was deeply touched.

Something that had been always lacking in his life—a real friend and companion, a partner of his mind and spirit—was now fulfilled in Clemens von Pirquet. They met nearly every day. They had time to talk. Slowly, gradually, they fell into step and rhythm together which was to produce in time a teamwork leading them both to the heights of greatness.

4

The differences, the contrast, between these two young men seemed almost too much. It was the most unlikely thing in the world that they should be friends. Dr. Pirquet was Catholic. Dr. Schick was Jewish. Dr. Pirquet was of the aristocracy. His family was well known at the court of the Hapsburg kings; they had large lands and wealth. Dr. Schick's family had neither fame nor fortune nor title. In the monarchy of Austria-Hungary a vast gulf separated aristocracy from other classes. An aristocrat commanded. Others obeyed.

Dr. Pirquet was tall and slim, with an urbane charm taught him by an etiquette handed down for centuries. Dr. Schick was of medium height, also slim, but shy with strangers, and unaware that he had a charm of his own in the kindness and simplicity of his nature.

Dr. Pirquet's mind flashed with brilliant ideas; his personality was impetuous and high strung. Dr. Schick was calmer, steadier. He distrusted his own brilliant intuition; he constantly checked it and studied it for flaws.

Yet with every day that passed these two grew closer together. They began with mutual respect and ended with the deepest of mutual affection.

They had no time to talk when they made the rounds with

Professor Escherich. Many times Béla's other work prevented him from coming. Their meeting place was the Outpatients' Clinic, to which Professor Escherich rarely came and which was, as customarily, turned over to his volunteer workers.

"You must have had younger brothers or sisters, Béla, to handle children as expertly as you do," remarked Dr. Pirquet one day as the two of them entered the Outpatients' Clinic. He smiled at the waiting patients. Here came, daily, the mothers with children who had minor ailments and did not need to be confined to bed. They were the poor of Graz. They could not afford a private physician. Dr. Pirquet bent over and tousled the hair of a small boy who was on his third visit, to have a burned arm rebandaged. "How are you feeling?" he asked. "Good. Just wait a moment and we will be with you."

He followed Béla into the office where they could put on their white doctors' jackets. "Not even Dr. Escherich can quiet a crying child the way you can," he went on, pursuing his earlier thought.

Struggling with a stubborn sleeve of his jacket which did not want to let his hand slip through, Béla said, "They don't particularly like me," panting and pulling at the jacket, "any more than they like anyone else. It's just that I like *them*. There!" he got the jacket on straight, looked up and smiled. "I really do. I'm never bored for one moment, talking to a child or listening to one. They are so honest. They have such imagination. I like to listen to them experiment with words and ideas."

"I like them too, but I don't always have your patience with them." Pirquet changed to a very serious tone. "That child with cerebral hypertrophy, whose brain cells are enlarged, died yesterday. I was with him until two this morning. You were particularly interested in his case, weren't you?"

"Yes, and there was another one—I've made some observations on both of them," said Béla.

"Written notes? Were they unusual cases? Are you planning to write them up for publication?" As he saw the look of embarrassment on Béla's face, Clemens Pirquet urged: "You must. Don't be modest. If you have seen something others haven't, or if you have made a more complete observation, it is your duty to have it printed."

They went out to the patients. After the boy's arm was bandaged, a little girl was brought in by her mother. The girl had a bad cough. Dr. Pirquet examined throat and chest, but even before that he had given Béla that quick, upward, distressed glance that told the story: tuberculosis. "You will have to take her to the hospital," he gently told the mother, "where they will accept infectious cases. Don't cry; she will be all right."

"It is the money," the mother sobbed. "I have no money for hospitals."

"That hospital," he said, writing down the name, "will not charge you. They will take your little girl—free."

The woman was fierce in her pride. "We do not want charity, Herr Doctor!"

Béla watched with interested reaction to what Dr. Pirquet would say. Could such a wealthy man understand the pride of poor people?

"A child's health," Dr. Pirquet answered the mother, "should never be a question of money. If the state pays for her care, the state benefits. If your daughter is out of the hospital, walking around with tuberculosis, she can infect others."

He picked up the woman's toilworn hands. "You have worked hard all your life; the least you can expect in return for your honest, decent labor is the free care for your child." He looked at Béla. "Someday we will have a public health program that will be free, with no stigma of charity, so that parents will bring their children to us when an infection first starts. That will be medicine to prevent disease."

Béla was overjoyed to see that his friend was sensitive to the dignity and pride of the poor.

After the Outpatients Clinic was closed for the day Dr. Pirquet suggested they go to a cheerful, warm coffeehouse nearby. Yesterday Béla would have been embarrassed; today he said, quite plainly, that he could not afford the few pennies it would cost. Dr. Pirquet passed another test in Béla's mind; he did not suggest that he pay for both. He said, "Then let's go for a short walk in the park."

It was November and a chill wind was blowing, yet Dr. Pirquet never mentioned it. The two walked up and down the paths, between trees that had shed their leaves and had a wintery look. The two men were so engrossed in talk they scarcely noticed.

Béla opened his heart to Clemens. He told him of his father and how good his uncle had been to him; how he hated disappointing them both; how he had reached a compromise by working for Professor Kraus.

"I see," said Dr. Pirquet. "I, too, had to defy the wishes of my parents, especially my mother, to become a doctor. It was not easy. For three years I gave in to them. My mother, I am afraid, had great ambitions for me, more worldly than churchly. She saw me, not as a humble priest, but a bishop or a cardinal. I have nothing against the religious life, but I soon realized

I had no true vocation for it. There was," he smiled, "great consternation and upheaval when I announced I was quitting the theological school, after three years study, to start all over again at medical school."

"You made the right decision. You have a genius for diagnosis."

"And what of you?" the other challenged. "You admit that working in the Bacteriology Department is a compromise. Oh, I know you could do well there, but with your special gift and interest in children, I think you will have to make a decision for pediatrics sooner or later."

"It is more difficult than you think. I am twenty-four years old and still dependent upon my father for every mouthful of food I eat," said Béla. He pulled the woolen scarf tighter around his throat.

"So am I." Clemens Pirquet laughed. "I know it is not the same thing; my father can spare it. Here we are, two men who hope to set the medical world on fire, yet that man over there," indicating a shopkeeper standing in his doorway across the street from the park, "would call us a couple of no-good wasters."

"How do you like working as a volunteer under Professor Escherich?" Béla asked, to get away from the distressing subject of his own problems.

"He's doing such splendid work. I learn so much every day. Right now he's doing investigations, insisting that bacteria is the cause of diarrhea in children, quarreling with some very eminent researchers who don't believe him. Have you read his published papers on tetany?"

From that point the two plunged into medical discussion. They found that their two minds sharpened against each other.

Dr. Pirquet tossed out a question relating to tuberculosis. Dr. Schick debated it, turning it over and over; challenged by another thought expressed by Clemens Pirquet. Out of such arguments they would pick the true kernels of ideas from the shells.

Béla was almost happy. His mind was stimulated and alive. Though he could spend only part of his time in the Children's Clinic, he knew he was of value to Professor Escherich and he was flattered by that great man's interest in his paper on cerebral hypertrophy. Béla was writing that paper slowly, testing over and over his observations.

Then the blow fell, and it was sudden and unexpected. Professor Escherich announced, very early in the year of 1902, that he had been invited to go to the University of Vienna to be Professor of Children's Diseases and head of the University Children's Clinic. It was a big step upward for him. The Viennese university was enormous, compared to the one in Graz.

For Béla it was a tragedy. He was about to lose his teacher and his friend because Dr. Pirquet would go to Vienna, too. Pirquet had now completed his term as volunteer and Professor Escherich had promised him that he would be a *Sekundar*, in charge of the hospital for infectious diseases.

"You won't come?" Pirquet asked Béla. "Escherich wants you; he said so."

"I can't. My father's business is not improving. He could not possibly afford extra money to maintain me in Vienna," Béla answered. He had never been so miserable, but he forced himself to smile. "We shall meet sometimes, Clemens. I shall watch the medical journals for your name. I know you are going to do great things."

After they were gone the desolation was more than Béla could bear. Professor Kraus was actually giving him the work of an assistant, though not the title. Anyone else would have been gratified with such an honor. It was not ingratitude but a sure knowledge that pediatrics was his real life.

Out of his despair came the solution. Would he have to eat more in Vienna than he did at home? Could he not eat less, perhaps, and thus save what he needed for rent?

"If you could possibly spare me just what I am costing you now—not one cent more—I could go to Vienna." He spoke to his parents that evening on what he considered a reasonable proposition. "It is more important to me to work under Professor Escherich than I can tell you. I wish I could explain, but all I can say is that it is vital."

"You are mad!" His father exclaimed. "Your food in this house, even the small amount of clothes you buy, does not amount to more than fifty kronen a month. You could not possibly live on that, and I could not possibly give you more than that."

"Béla, you would starve," his mother said. "What kind of a place could you live in, on so little?"

Fifty kronen equaled about five dollars in American money. It was true that five dollars bought a great deal more in those days; still, it was a pitifully small sum.

"It would be enough, Mamma. I can get good, hearty meals in the hospital dining room." He was not sure he could but he had to set his mother's fears at rest. "I will find a family who will be glad to give me a good, clean room for a few kronen a month. Why, I will be rich. I'll be able to buy flowers for all those girls you want me to marry."

His mother smiled fondly at him, then she sighed. She had

hatched a strange duckling in her brood of chickens. It was hard for her to understand Béla.

Jacques Schick was determined to put an end to this nonsense, once and for all. "You are no sooner settled with Professor Kraus than you want to change again. Now I want to know what is going on in your mind, Béla. Are you mad?" Béla realized this was a crucial moment for him. He must try to make them both see what was driving him in one direction. "I want to work with children," he began. "I have always wanted to. This is not a change; it is a natural step. My life was always leading me to the children. Papa, if you could see the sick babies and how their eyes look at you, begging you to get rid of the pain for them. Mamma, you know how grateful you are to Uncle Sigismund because he has saved all of your children from sickness—think of the thousands of children who don't have an Uncle Sigismund."

Now Béla was hardly aware of his parents. He was almost talking to himself. "When I am separated from the children in the hospital, they come to me in my dreams and they cry out to me for help, but I'm not there to help them. For some reason I have been given a skill in my hands that sets me apart and makes me a doctor of children. Must I let that skill slip away? If I do, somewhere, some place, a child will die because I am not there. I will hear that child's voice all my life."

His attention came back to the utter stillness in the room. His parents were looking at him with eyes wide and amazed. For once Jacques Schick was speechless, Janka's mouth was trembling.

"Help me to go to Vienna," Béla asked them. "Papa, I know you—if you saw a child fall down in the street you would stop and pick it up, no matter how busy you were. If a child

needed you, you would help. I am not asking you to help me,
but those little ones in the beds in the hospitals."

It was a few seconds before Jacques Schick spoke. Then he
must blow his nose first, to hide the fact that tears were close.
"I didn't know," he said, humbly. "I didn't know. I wish I
could give you more than fifty kronen, Béla. I wish it were
five hundred kronen. Stop crying, Janka, we have to get this
boy ready to go to Vienna."

One week later Dr. Béla Schick walked down the beautiful
streets of the Ring in Vienna. Hanging from one arm was his
suitcase, clutched in the other were his notebooks, too precious
to be shipped from Graz. It was a cold day. He walked fast,
and his genuine pleasure and excitement in being in this most
beautiful of cities kept him warm.

He was young enough to enjoy everything he saw about
him. From the coffeehouses came music and laughter, the rich
smell of pastries and the invitation of coffee or hot chocolate
topped with whipped cream. He hadn't a single groschen to
spend for such pleasures; he was free, though, to look and sniff
the air and smile at the singing and laughter of gay Vienna.

The magnificent sculptures he passed were there as much
for his enjoyment as for the richest citizen. He could admire
the baroque architecture of the Opera House and the famous
buildings of the Court. In the shop windows glowed jewels
and rich art treasures; he had no desire to possess them, only
to admire them.

Though a bachelor and much too busy for courtships, Béla's
heart was quickened by the sight of so many beautiful women.
He watched as horse-drawn carriages went past. He thought
he had never seen such loveliness, such furs, such jewels, such

outrageously saucy hats. In front of a theater one of the carriages stopped. A footman in blue and white livery, smart as paint, stepped down from his high box and opened the carriage door for the lady. In doing so he rudely shouldered Béla aside, but any resentment the young doctor might have felt was forgotten in the pleasure of seeing such a pretty lady in a red velvet jacket carrying fresh violets.

He went on. His way took him out of the more fashionable section and now he began to think of what lay ahead. It came, suddenly, as a shock, that Professor Escherich did not know he had arrived and might not want him! When Béla walked up the imposing steps of the vast University of Vienna and inquired the way to the Pediatrics Department, his heart was beginning to be troubled. He had left Graz impetuously. He had not tried to write or find out if he would be welcomed here. Professor Escherich was then the foremost pediatrician in the world; students flocked to him; any young doctor would consider himself fortunate to work as a volunteer under him.

The office door with the severe sign on it: HEAD, PEDIATRIC DEPARTMENT, was open. Béla glanced in. Professor Escherich was seated at his desk, looking even more formidable and more distinguished than he had at the University of Graz.

He looked up. He saw Béla. He rose and came forward with outstretched hands, a most unusual welcome for so restrained a man. "Béla!" he cried. "Are you visiting us? or—" he saw the suitcase "—or are you here to stay?"

"If you will have me, Herr Professor, I should like to be a volunteer under you." Emotion was making Béla more shy and he spoke in a low, hesitant voice. "I have left Graz."

"If I will have you? Do not talk nonsense. I have been

hoping that you would come. Dr. Pirquet has now finished his term as volunteer with me. As *Sekundar*, he is in charge of the St. Anna Hospital. You will work under him. It will be splendid for both of you. The St. Anna has isolated wards for infectious cases of scarlet fever and diphtheria and tuberculosis, which neither of you has had much opportunity to study before."

Clemens Pirquet was even more overjoyed to see Béla than the professor was. He came into the office as the two finished talking, embraced Béla warmly, and insisted upon taking him immediately to see the St. Anna Hospital.

As the two walked down the street and around the corner, Dr. Pirquet could not hold back his enthusiasm.

"Think of it, Béla!—the two of us working together, making rounds together as we used to, making our investigations together. Even now I think I have stumbled upon something which needs your help." They came to the St. Anna and walked into a large, broad courtyard. Béla saw for the first time the sprawling, unlovely buildings which would be the center of his life for so many years to come.

As they walked straight ahead to a stairway on the far side, Dr. Pirquet indicated the building on their left with a sign saying SCARLET FEVER; another, similar one on their right read DIPHTHERIA. They went up the stairway and turned into the general ward which was built out so that it extended part way over the courtyard. Behind the general ward was the library.

Dr. Pirquet would have led Béla there. He wanted to talk. "Let me tell you about my problem—"

"Let me first see the children," said Béla, putting his suitcase and papers down on the floor. "Let me see the children, please."

The tense, eager face of Dr. Pirquet softened. He looked at the younger man and smiled apologetically. "You are right, Béla. Always and ever, it must be '*first* the children.'"

Through ward after ward, building after building, they went. The heart and spirit of Béla Schick was at peace. He was finally where he belonged. Here were his children: the very sick, who could not lift their flushed or pallid faces from their pillows; the convalescents, who looked at him and were instantly happy, recognizing in this doctor a friend; and those almost ready to leave the hospital whose restlessness was appeased when Béla Schick took them, one by one, onto his lap.

He told them of his walk that morning and the carriages and beautiful women he had seen, and all the things in the shop windows. It was a fairy story to the children. They were poor. In those days any parent who could afford to do so kept their children at home even during infectious illnesses.

Finally they came to the scarlet fever building. Dr. Pirquet led Béla to the bed of one child. The little patient was tossing, restlessly, in fever. His hands constantly went to his abdomen, to try to scratch the red eruption on it, while a nurse gently tried to persuade the child to stop.

"Do you see?" Dr. Pirquet asked in a low voice. "Would you say that those symptoms of fever and rash and hives were scarlet fever symptoms?"

Béla leaned over to examine closely, then shook his head. "No. I have had little experience, clinically, with scarlet fever cases but that is not a scarlatina rash. I believe I have read some place of this rash, which is called exanthema, and which appears after an injection. I don't think there is much written about it because it seems to come for no special reason and disappears just as irrationally. It is irritating but not dangerous, I believe."

"That is correct, but it is not irrational. I have been studying it, Béla, and I believe it is definitely caused by something in the serum we inject—not by the antitoxin, but by the serum. I have found, I think, that it has a definite period of incubation. It happens to only a few children. Why? Why not to all? And why does it always appear about eight to twelve days after the injection? What is it? I don't call it exanthema because that word means only the rash; actually the symptoms are much more varied and severe. There are usually fever, rash and hives, and I suspect that swollen glands are a part of it, though I am not sure. I call this 'serum sickness.' "

"We will investigate, Clemens. We will find out all about this serum sickness." Béla leaned down once more. His foot hooked a chair closer to the bed and he sat down, studying the child for several long moments, without speaking. Then he looked up and there was that look in his face which his friend had hoped to find—a puzzled, thoughtful, brooding look, profoundly absorbed. "Yes, this is very strange indeed. Clemens, I must go now and find a place to live, but I will return here this evening. I will go to the library and read everything I can find on this subject."

"Tonight? Your first night in Vienna? Surely you want to see something of the theaters or the opera or—no? Then I will cancel my engagement for this evening and we will both begin our studies in the library. Shall we say eight o'clock?" asked Dr. Pirquet.

Béla nodded. As the two men parted, one to search for a room, the other to the laboratory, they looked at each other and in the eyes of both was the same look of great happiness. They would be working together.

And even, when later that day Béla finally found a room near the hospital at a price he could afford to pay, his spirits were not dimmed by the extreme poverty and ugliness of it. It didn't matter to him that its only window looked onto a corridor, giving poor light and air, or that the mattress on his bed was of straw, that there was no heat whatsoever in the room and only a pitcher of water for washing and drinking.

He would sleep here and that was all. His real home would be the St. Anna Hospital.

5

By the spring of 1902, Dr. Schick and Dr. Pirquet were well established in the routine of work at the St. Anna Hospital for Children. Clemens Pirquet was in charge, while Béla acted as his Volunteer, an unpaid assistant.

Actually, the different positions meant little to either of them. They made the rounds together. They worked as the closest of friends and partners. They divided up the work and the responsibility as the need arose.

In addition to the daily care of the sick children, they shared the intense excitement of their explorations into serum sickness.

What was it? What was this strange illness which affected some children—but not others—after they received injections against scarlet fever or diphtheria? Was there a pattern to it or was it just freak chance? What were its symptoms? Could it be cured?

Other doctors and medical researchers had noticed this strange sickness but only a few of them had paid much attention.

"I read of two men, one named Heubner and the other, Bokay, who seemed to think the cause was the substance in the serum, not in the antitoxin. That is what I think also," Dr.

76

Pirquet said, as he and Béla sat together over the noon meal in the hospital dining room.

It was May and the windows were open to the warm air. From outside in the hospital garden came the pleasant voice of a nurse and the sounds of laughing children. "Another man, Johannesen," continued Dr. Pirquet, "has suggested it is the protein in the serum. I am inclined to believe it."

Dr. Schick nodded. "I've been studying the statistics of Hartung. From more than six thousand cases, he found approximately ten per cent suffered from what we call serum sickness. He only classified those with hives and rash. I believe there are more, and that fever, swelling, pains in the joints are also symptoms of this sickness."

A nurse called Dr. Pirquet away. While he was gone Béla ate a hearty lunch, since he would be able to afford only coffee and bread for breakfast and dinner. His mind was not on the food, however, but on serum sickness.

He went back in his mind to Professor Kraus's classes and the lectures. Both diphtheria and scarlet fever were diseases caused by the toxic poison—one of the diphtheria bacilli, the other of the scarlet fever streptococci. The treatment for both was somewhat the same. A horse would be injected so that it developed a mild case of either diphtheria or scarlet fever; the horse's body would naturally develop antitoxins to combat the disease. When they knew there were a lot of these antitoxins in the blood, there would be withdrawn—without hurting the horse—a quantity of serum. Serum was the thin, liquid stuff of the blood, without the red cells.

Inside that serum were the antitoxins. The serum was then cooked. There were many varieties of scarlet fever and the strength of the dosage and the length of cooking time varied.

For diphtheria, there was always a long period of cooking, so that a weak dose would result.

When a child was already ill with either diphtheria or scarlet fever, the child's body was producing antitoxins to fight the poisonous toxins of the bacteria. If the toxins were weak and the antitoxins strong, then the child recovered quickly and the parents sometimes never knew the child had had anything worse than a sore throat or a slight fever or rash.

But if the toxins were stronger, then the child needed help. Doctors could inject the serum, with the extra antitoxins the horse had created, and these would join in with the body's defense army to defeat the murdering, killing poisons of the toxins.

Dr. Schick drank a glass of milk and then held up the empty glass and looked at it.

The body, he told himself, takes in foreign proteins all the time, harmlessly. We eat eggs. We drink milk. We eat meat. All these have proteins. In the digestive tract were enzymes and other substances which could handle these proteins and by digestion change them into amino acids and turn them into proper food for the body.

Serum had proteins in it as part of the substance of the blood. If that serum were taken into the mouth and stomach of a child it would be easily digested. But an injection under the skin was not natural. There were no digestive substances at the point of entry of the injection needle; the serum was not traveling through the body into the stomach. Dr. Pirquet was convinced it was these foreign proteins which were causing this strange rash and fever and swellings. Certainly they were not the symptoms of either diphtheria or scarlet fever themselves, though they had confused most medical men.

They must be caused, somehow, by the proteins in the serum of the horse, which was introduced into the child's body by injection.

Dr. Pirquet returned from his errand and the two men picked up their discussion where it had left off. "Béla, what is our theory so far? One, that it is the proteins in the serum which are causing the mischief. Two, some children react and get sick; others don't. Three, serum sickness is not fatal; we cannot stop making injections because of it; the antitoxin in the serum is too desperately needed to save the children from death or the severe illness of diphtheria or scarlet fever."

"What we have," Béla interrupted, "are two diseases—the diphtheria or scarlet fever, and the serum sickness. One kills, the other does not. But we are going to have to prove it, Clemens. We'll have to study case after case, to be sure. Most doctors just assume that there are not two sicknesses, but one; everything is due to the injection of the antitoxin and the fight going on in the body between toxins and antitoxins."

They knew this was not true. Dr. Pirquet had already found that the antitoxin they injected went to work immediately. Usually within twelve hours after injection the child's fever would rise. The battle inside the child would mount in intensity. Then, just as suddenly, the crisis of either diphtheria or scarlet fever would come and the child would begin to get well. It was much later—six to eight days afterward—that this strange serum sickness would set in. Dr. Pirquet had spotted that this was an incubation period, during which the child's system could develop antibodies to fight against, destroy and digest the foreign proteins.

When the system had formed these defense antibodies and they encountered the proteins in the serum, then the battle of serum sickness started and the poor children broke out into rashes and fevers and swellings.

"I only wish we knew why some children get it and others don't. Is it the kind of serum, the amount of serum or the age of different serums? Does it have something to do with the severity of the diphtheria or scarlet fever attack?" Dr. Pirquet asked, very much puzzled.

"I am thinking that it is more likely because some children are more sensitive to proteins than others are." This thought had been slowly taking form in Béla's mind.

Dr. Pirquet stared at him. His eyes grew excited. He stubbed out his cigarette. "That's it! I'm almost sure it is. That would explain, for example, why those two last diphtheria patients, Leopold and Rosa, who were sister and brother, had almost identical symptoms of serum sickness. They both had hives on the seventh day after injection; both had fever; the fever dropped for both on the eighth day; then there was a sudden rise again and both recovered almost at the same moment."

Béla nodded. He had taken to wearing glasses because constant reading tired his eyes. Yet behind those glasses there was no concealing the deep brightness of his blue eyes, contrasting oddly with the shadows of fatigue around them. "Yes, in that case both children would have the same physical inheritance. Though it may not always hold true, it is likely that children of the same family would have about the same sensitivity, or lack of it, to proteins." He rose. "I must go to the laboratory. I have five new rabbits which I injected yesterday—"

They went to the door, still talking of their research.

This idea of Dr. Béla Schick's, that certain children (and later, it would be proved true for adults as well) had peculiar sensitivity to proteins was to have a far-reaching result that neither doctor then could have predicted. Someday, from this discovery, it would even be understood why a twelve-year-old Béla Schick would have terribly swollen eyes and face from the sting of a bee, while some other child would have only a slight discomfort.

That was in the future. Right now the two doctors were not trying to prophesy the future. They were too busy exploring serum sickness.

All the children admitted to the scarlet fever or the diphtheria buildings were very sick children. This meant that every one of them had to be given an injection of the horse serum, to supply the added antitoxins the child lacked to defeat these diseases. Most of the children recovered without any symptoms of serum sickness, or with just a little fever around the sixth or eighth day. It was the other cases which especially interested Dr. Schick and Dr. Pirquet.

In those cases, the antibodies formed during that incubation period did not easily digest and destroy the proteins. Instead, the meeting of the antibodies with the proteins stirred up a lot of trouble for the children, giving off acids and poisons and irritations which produced the hives and fever and itchings and swellings.

Some of the children just itched and scratched; some just had fever; some had swellings. Others had combinations of these. One patient, little Hans had everything. He proved their theories, but they were not happy about it, because the child was as miserable as a child could be.

On the sixth day after the injection the glands in the groin were enlarged to the size of beans. Bumps collected around them. The skin of his abdomen was red. By the tenth day his fever was high; he broke out into a terrible rash; his cheeks looked as if they were on fire.

"He's had the same amount of serum and the same kind with which we injected other children on the same day, yet they've had no symptoms while he has them all. I think we have to say that the amount of serum is a minor factor. With very large doses we do have a higher percentage of children who get serum sickness. Yet your point, Béla," said Dr. Pirquet, as the two doctors met Professor Escherich in the courtyard to discuss the progress of their work with him, "is correct. It is the child's own organism which is more or less sensitive to proteins."

"Luckily, we know little Hans will recover. Serum sickness is not fatal, but it is not pleasant to watch a tiny boy suffer like that," said Béla. "All we can do is try to cool his fever a bit, rub the hives with menthol alcohol, and put Burow's solution on the swellings." Speaking particularly to Professor Escherich, he added, "What is important is that we are now sure of certain things: one, it is the protein in the serum which causes the illness; two, that there is an incubation period while the body is developing the substances to take care of the proteins; three, that some children have special sensitivity—hypersensitivity—to proteins."

"Do all the cases run to this pattern?" asked Professor Escherich. He was intensely interested. Another man might have thought that Pirquet and Schick were wasting their time and his budget, because Professor Escherich was responsible for money and salaries and the work.

The St. Anna Hospital was supported by private wealth. It was a Catholic institution for poor children and its nurses were Catholic Sisters. Yet, under the laws of Austria-Hungary, the doctors of St. Anna were paid by the government and Professor Escherich was held accountable for funds, expenditures, and the work of his assistants, as well as those of the university medical department of which he was head.

The Empire was generous with money because Professor Escherich's reputation was great. However, they expected spectacular results from him and his young men. They wanted new sensational discoveries of bacilli, or wonderful cures that would redound to the credit of Vienna and eclipse the medical prestige of Berlin or Paris.

Yes, he might well have said that serum sickness was not important. Only a small percentage of patients suffered from it. What would it contribute to the progress of medicine? Professor Escherich had no such doubts. Of all the brilliant young doctors in Vienna who worked under him, he had greatest hopes from these two.

He repeated his question. "Do all the cases run to this pattern?" He had seen a swift glance exchanged between Dr. Pirquet and Dr. Schick.

"No." Dr. Pirquet had to be honest. "We have run across two baffling cases. Two children, Elizabeth and Alexandrine, broke out with serum sickness almost immediately upon getting the injection. We don't understand this."

"You will." Professor Escherich was positive. "There is always a reason, always a cause, for what the body does. You will find it." Austere, dignified, distinguished in appearance, he settled his hat on his head and said good-by. As he reached the courtyard gate he turned and smiled at them. "Good luck, gentlemen."

They felt they needed some luck when, in July of that same year, 1902, they encountered another case as baffling to them as were the cases of Elizabeth and Alexandrine they had mentioned to Professor Escherich.

Three-year-old Heinrich was admitted to the scarlet fever building, quite ill, and received his first injection of scarlet fever serum. The crisis of that illness passed and on the eighth day he showed symptoms of serum sickness. Now he became one of their "specials" whose case was to be watched, notes taken, and a case history written up for the papers they must someday write on serum sickness. Heinrich's symptoms lasted for six days and then the itching and fever stopped and he was well.

On July 15th while he was convalescing and still in the hospital they decided to immunize him against diphtheria.

That same afternoon, after getting the injection, he broke out into hives. By the next morning his arm was swollen and the tissues full of fluid. Once more, as in the cases of Elizabeth and Alexandrine, there had been an *immediate* reaction without any period of incubation.

How could this be? Were all their theories wrong? Dr. Schick wrote it down on the chart and looked at what he had written, in exasperation. Days and nights of hospital work, study, research in the library, experiments in the laboratory—none of these could explain why these three children should react differently from others who showed symptoms of serum sickness.

His whole life was absorbed in his work. In addition to his serum sickness research and to his large medical responsibilities in the hospital wards, taking care of all the children, he was also getting his earlier study on cerebral hypertrophy ready for publication. He was studying, too, every detail of scarlet fever and diphtheria, for future research.

When he left the hospital it was for the laboratory. When he left the laboratory, it was to go to the library. At dinner time he went home to his room, stopping first at a small shop where he was known. There he bought bread.

It was customary in food shops, in poor districts of Vienna, to break a loaf of bread in half and sell each half for a penny. One half was always rounded and bigger than the other, and the proprietor of this shop liked Béla so he always saved the big half for him. Béla would hurry with his purchase to his cold, dimly lit room, brew himself a cup of coffee and warm his fingers around it. The coffee and bread were his dinner.

He hardly noticed what he was eating, because he had a book propped open to read. After his hunger was a bit satisfied he would go back to the hospital to make the evening rounds of the wards.

Clemens Pirquet was no less busy, though his life was more comfortable. Being the *Sekundar*, he lived at the hospital.

There were only twenty-four hours a day. How could they do so much and work so continuously? They were young. Dr. Pirquet could well have afforded the money to enjoy all the temptations of the romantic Vienna—the lighthearted, party-loving Vienna which danced every night to Strauss waltzes. Dr. Schick didn't have to work as an unpaid volunteer. He could have gone into private practice and made money, to enjoy the life of Vienna.

Theirs was a different world. They treated the children of the poor. Money and popularity meant nothing to either of them.

From his liberal-minded father and his warmhearted mother, Béla had inherited humane, unselfish ideals. Freiherr Peter Clemens von Pirquet—to give him his full title—had found those same ideals for himself. He had learned with his own heart and eyes that suffering had nothing to do with class. A sick child was just as much in need of tenderness and love and care, whether that child was high- or lowborn.

Clemens Pirquet was unusual in another respect. The class into which he had been born was full of prejudice. They looked with contempt upon other people as not as good as they. Working with as fine a man as Béla Schick had taught Dr. Pirquet that birth did not make a man superior. He had come to love Béla Schick as a brother, and Béla returned that feeling.

In spite of their hard work, they did not feel deprived of the good things of life. They were happy in what they were doing. They were fully alive. Each morning Béla woke with a sense of hurry and eagerness. He must get up quickly, get dressed, drink his coffee, gulp down the dry bread and then hurry to the hospital.

Occasionally Professor Escherich would call upon one or the other of them to do short-term work with one of his other assistants, or these other men would help at St. Anna. There was the brainy Dr. Moser, who had perfected a serum for scarlet fever injections; there was Dr. Franz Hamburger and Dr. August von Reuss.

In the beginning of the year 1903 Béla Schick published two articles in medical journals, one of them, on cerebral hypertrophy in children, which he had begun while he was still in Graz. The other was on the variability of diphtheria bacillus. They were well received. Professor Escherich complimented him on making two important, if small, contributions to pediatric knowledge.

He was also becoming very well liked at the hospital. When

he knew people he was not at all shy. He had a natural charm of manner; he was thoughtful and kind, and had a whimsical sense of humor. The nursing Sisters adored him and worried over his lack of comforts and good meals.

In February of 1903 came an opportunity to test their theories with a number of children at the same time, rather than just observing a single case. In the General Ward of noninfectious diseases one child suddenly showed suspicious signs of coming down with diphtheria. This meant it would be necessary to immunize the entire ward. They were sure some of the children would have serum sickness, while others would not.

They would take the children in groups. Dr. Pirquet insisted upon giving himself an injection, along with the first group, so that he could compare his symptoms with the children's. He knew already that he was susceptible to serum sickness. Nine months before he had injected himself with two hundred cc. of scarlet fever serum, and eight days after that he had developed hives and pains in his joints.

The General Ward now became their laboratory. On February 11, at 6:00 P.M. Dr. Schick gave seven injections of exactly the same amount of the same diphtheria serum. Of the seven there were three—Dr. Pirquet and two girls, Johanna and Emilie, who had had previous injections. The other four had not.

Once the injections were given the two doctors worked for a while in the other wards, and then came back to the General Ward to wait and talk. The injections of horse serum they had given contained diphtheria antitoxin. They knew well what was happening inside the bodies of the six children and Pirquet: the antitoxin was going throughout the system.

If by any chance there was a diphtheria bacillus, spreading its deadly poison into the throat of any one of them, those antibodies would take care of it. Even if not, all seven would be immune for many months, perhaps a year or more, now that there were antitoxins in the body.

There would be no sign of serum sickness for a period of six to eight days, at least. But during that period the body would be manufacturing the substances to digest and destroy the serum proteins.

This should have been the pattern. To their amazement, as they sat and talked that night, first Johanna and then Emilie woke up, crying and fretful. Dr. Schick went to the bedside of one while Dr. Pirquet attended the other. Both little girls had the same pale, doughlike swellings on their forearms and were in pain.

"They are symptoms of serum sickness!" Dr. Pirquet's whisper was an exclamation. They carried their candles over to the other four sleeping children. They showed no signs of serum sickness.

Dr. Pirquet was rubbing his own arm. It was already itching with rash.

"Look!" He showed it to Béla. "All three of us, Johanna, Emilie and I, have had an immediate reaction, with no incubation period whatsoever."

Five hours later Dr. Pirquet's arm was greatly swollen and extremely painful. He carefully wrote down all the symptoms, ignoring the pain, while Dr. Schick soothed the two little girls, bathing their feverish faces with a cool solution.

There was no question, the next day, that all three had had an immediate onset of serum sickness. There was also no explanation for it. Of the other four of the group, two showed symptoms of serum sickness at the end of a week and the other two showed none at all.

Dr. Schick took the medical histories of all seven and spread them out on the desk in front of him. Here was everything they knew about each one: age, sex, name, names of parents, previous diseases. Perhaps somewhere in these histories there might be a clue.

As he started to put down Emilie's card, suddenly something struck him as being important. He picked it up again, studied one line on it, and then went out of his office to the General Ward and then down the room to Emilie's bed. "Emilie," he asked, "tell me, did you have a sickness called smallpox not very long ago?"

"Mamma thought I had it. She took me to a doctor," answered the little girl.

"Did the doctor do what we did—stick a needle in your arm and give you an injection?"

The child nodded. Dr. Schick straightened up, feeling sure that the idea which had suddenly struck him was correct. He knew that Johanna had had an injection against scarlet fever only six weeks ago; that showed on her chart. He could hardly wait until Dr. Pirquet came downstairs from the tuberculosis patients.

"Clemens, listen, this is important. All three of you had previous injections of serum, not long ago. The other four we injected had not. We know that the body has produced a substance, antibodies, to destroy the protein in the serum. What if those antibodies are still present—still free, still powerful—in the body a long time afterward? Now, when we give a second injection there is no need for an incubating period. Those antibodies move to destroy the proteins in the serum within hours."

"Let's consider this." Still rubbing his arm and glancing now and then at the great swelling of it, Dr. Pirquet was paying alert attention to what Béla had said. "We know that the antitoxin results in immunity for a long period, for both or either scarlet fever and diphtheria. If what you are saying is right, then perhaps this is also the explanation of immunity. The antitoxin, and the other antibodies which digest the protein, remain—as you say, *free*—in the system, ready to move to the spot of attack."

He opened his mouth to receive the thermometer which Dr. Schick gave him, and listened as Béla, walking back and forth behind his desk, continued to think out loud. "While I was waiting for you I got out the case histories of Alexandrine and Elizabeth and Heinrich, those cases which baffled us before. It was the same story with them. All had had previous injections a few months before we gave them a *second* one. That was why they had no incubation period; why they reacted immediately with symptoms of serum sickness."

Without bothering to read his temperature Dr. Pirquet grabbed it out of his mouth and said: "You've found the answer, then! I am sure of it."

It was still a theory, but now they knew what to watch for. Another group of children were injected. It was the same experience: one child in that group had had a previous injection of serum and that child reacted immediately with serum sickness while others did not. Another child, who had also had a previous injection did not get sick from the serum but, like good detectives, they investigated and found that she had not had serum sickness before, either. She had little sensitivity to proteins.

However, just as they were becoming certain that this theory answered the puzzle, another strange case appeared. A boy whose name was Egon, who had had a previous injection and had had serum sickness the first time, did not react with the symptoms immediately. He did get them, with a much shorter incubation period, but not immediately.

They had no answer for this as yet, but Dr. Schick could not put Egon out of his mind. He had a feeling that the little boy's body was trying to tell him something.

In that year of 1903, together they wrote and published the first steps of their discovery, leaving out what happened after the second injection, which had to be proved by more cases. The titles of their published papers were: *The Theory of Incubation*, followed by *The Theory of Vaccination*.

Their discovery of the immediate reaction following the second injection opened wide the field of their investigations. It would also give to the world a new understanding of the process of how the body became immune.

"Antibodies," as they used the word, meant any substance the body created in itself to fight against harmful invaders. Antitoxin was one form of antibody. They were sure now that, just as the antitoxin injected into the child stayed there for a long time and therefore kept the child immune, so also did the natural antitoxin created by the child.

It accounted for the fact that a great many children had slight attacks of diseases and were thereafter immune—such a child could sleep beside her sister who had diphtheria, and not get it. This would be true of other diseases besides the toxic ones. Some bacteria caused disease without giving off toxins;

in these the child's system would develop antibodies which would remain after the disease was gone, to make the child immune.

Dr. Schick and Dr. Pirquet felt they had come a long, long way with their understanding of disease, incubation periods and immunity. But what about Egon? Why had one child reacted so strangely?

In March a little girl named Emma was admitted to the diphtheria building. The ugly, gray membrane was already in her throat; she was seriously ill. She was given an injection of serum.

Dr. Schick already knew her history. She had been in the hospital nine months ago with scarlet fever. She had been given an injection and had developed serum sickness, after an unusually long incubation period. But if his theory of immediate reaction were true, then this time Emma should have serum sickness right away.

He had found it didn't matter if the first injection was for a different disease. The substance the body had created to digest the serum protein would still be there to destroy these new proteins of the new injection.

Emma, like Egon, did not react immediately. It was seven days before any swelling showed. The incubation period was shorter than it had been for the first injection, but it certainly wasn't immediate.

Sitting beside Emma's bed, Dr. Schick was so lost in thought that the nurse walked around him and had to bend over him to take Emma's temperature.

He looked up. "I'm sorry, Sister. I am in your way."

"That is all right, Herr Doctor. Your thinking is what is

important to us all. I only wish you wouldn't work so hard."
She smiled at him.

Late that night when he was finally through at the hospital
and had gone home to lie shivering under the thin blankets of
his bed, he was still thinking of Emma and Egon. His thoughts
kept him from being too conscious of the cold and of the
hardness of his bed. He went back over every single thing he
knew about both children.

Something nagged at his brain. He pinned it down at last.
Time! Both Egon and Emma had had their first injections a
long time before the second. It had been nine months ago that
Emma had been in the hospital.

Could that be it? Could the antibody substances be weak?
No, he dismissed that thought. It wasn't likely. But suppose
there were actually no more antibodies in the system at all?
Suppose the body had learned how to react, with one experience, and therefore could create the new antibodies that much
quicker?

It was such an odd idea, but the next morning he found
himself returning to it over and over. He did not want to
discuss it with Dr. Pirquet yet. He went to the laboratory as
soon as he could.

There were several rabbits there to whom he had given injections nearly a year ago. He carefully withdrew a tiny drop
of blood from their ears and studied that blood under the
microscope. There were no antibodies present. Now he injected those same animals; it was their second.

Day after day he watched them. They did not have serum
sickness immediately, but they did have it in a much shorter
incubation time than they had for the first injection. They
behaved much as Egon and Emma had.

So one night, after first checking to see that little Emma and the others in the diphtheria building were all right, he went to Dr. Pirquet's office and told him of the startling supposition he had made and how the rabbits seemed to prove it.

"Are you saying that the body *remembers?*" Dr. Pirquet was at first incredulous. "The *mind* remembers, but with a conscious intelligence directing it. This would be an unconscious, mindless thing. Is the body able to remember, to learn from experience, in this case?" Doubtful at first, the more he thought of it, the more he was convinced. "Obviously those children had a quicker, an *accelerated*, reaction. Béla, I think you have discovered something so important that it may easily be the most valuable single thing so far in our theory. It seems to me," he said, his mind grappling brilliantly with these new ideas, "that it is not so much a case of the body remembering, as it is that the body is altered. Once a child has had an injection, even though a long time ago, the system of that child is never quite the same again. It is altered."

They talked it over with Professor Escherich. He decided that such a theory was possible, but it must be carefully researched and proved. He was proud of both of them and said so.

"It is rare for two men to work together as a team, as you do. I imagine you find it hard to know which of you first thinks of an idea and which one carries that one to the other. You are doing excellent work."

6

Several months later they sat together in the dining room of the St. Anna hospital. "How is little Eduard?" asked Dr. Pirquet.

Béla Schick laughed. "I hope the men who read our book on serum sickness will not be as skeptical as that rascal. He absolutely refuses to believe me when I tell him it is hives and rash which are itching him. He is sure they are fleas; he is quite shocked that a hospital should allow his bed to have fleas in it."

"I know. He told me he was not going to stay in that bed any more. There were animals in it!" Clemens smiled, then he turned the conversation to their usual one, work on serum sickness.

By taking a tiny drop of blood from children who had had injections from nine months to a year before and putting that drop under a microscope, they had proved there were no antibodies in it. Yet, when they had given the second injection, those who were hypersensitive to protein got the symptoms of serum sickness—earlier than they had the first time. Béla's idea was confirmed.

When they were through eating Dr. Schick took a paper sack from his pocket and put into it what was left of the chicken on his plate and also an uneaten roll. This had gradually become a habit with him, to be saved for his dinner. Without interrupting what he was saying, Dr. Pirquet handed over his own untouched chicken wing.

Neither man saw anything odd in this. Neither had false pride. Dr. Schick was now an intern at the St. Anna Hospital, receiving twenty-five kronen and his luncheon, but actually he was poorer than before. His father had run into business troubles and could no longer send him the fifty kronen every month.

Dr. Pirquet was indignant that a man of Dr. Schick's caliber should be paid so little, but that was the custom and it was the best Professor Escherich could do. So they both accepted the simple need for the leftover meats, without making a fuss about it.

What was poverty and the pinch of hunger, compared to being able to do the work one loved?

Dr. Schick went to the scarlet fever building that day with a light step and an eager heart. He would have liked to have had money, not so much for himself but for this hospital. He would have rebuilt these wards with lots of window space; with clean, painted walls instead of the old brown ones. He would have provided more light than the single, dim gaslight hanging from the ceiling. He knew that Professor Escherich was struggling with officials to get the money to build a new hospital.

What did it matter? Dr. Schick saw in the ward the children who wanted him and called for him; there were the kind, loving nursing Sisters who were so patient and whose means were as small as his own.

The whole year of 1904 was devoted to the compiling of

more case histories of children with serum sickness. Careful notes had to be taken of the results of first and second injections. By the coming of winter the two doctors knew they were ready to begin writing.

Just at this moment came extremely sad news for Béla. Dr. Telegdi had died. Uncle and nephew had seen very little of each other for several years, since both were busy, but they had not forgotten each other. They had written frequently. Béla felt the loss deeply. He felt he could repay all the help Uncle Sigismund had given him only by working harder than before.

The story and the theory which he and Dr. Pirquet were writing on "Serum Sickness" became a small book. They worked on it evenings in the library, writing and rewriting, always trying for the simplest way of saying what they had discovered. This was extremely important. They felt that if the alterations in the body after the first injection were understood, other doctors might go on from there to explore the questions of immunity and individual sensitivities.

They wrote the chapter on "Reinjection," the second injection, with painstaking care. Speaking of what happened, they wrote:

". . . we came to the conclusion that it was the human organism which has become specifically altered, due to the first injection of a foreign serum, and that it has acquired a new property in consequence of which the second reaction occurs more quickly than the first."

It was a proud moment when at last they could place the finished work on Professor Escherich's desk.

Dr. Béla Schick was only twenty-seven and Dr. Pirquet thirty. The medical world would consider them as young upstarts. They warned themselves about this. It didn't matter. It was only Professor Escherich's approval or disapproval which mattered to them. If he found no flaws in their discovery, they would be satisfied.

He took his time reading it. Not until some days later did he visit them at the St. Anna Hospital to announce that he was having "Serum Sickness" published.

"Very fine, original work, gentlemen," he said. "I am proud of you."

They both breathed easier.

It was a good thing that neither of the two doctors ever expected fame to burst like fireworks over their heads, because it didn't happen. A few medical journals commented with enthusiasm and praise. A few medical researchers wrote to Dr. Escherich for more information. A few medical universities urged their students to read it. That was all.

The big medical centers of Vienna, Berlin and Paris were friendly rivals—and sometimes not so friendly. There were fine schools in England but they did not have the reputation of the European ones. As for America!—it lagged so far behind that the brightest of its medical students took it as a matter of course that they would finish their studies in one of the European capitals if they could scrape up the money.

Neither Dr. Pirquet nor Dr. Schick had expected great fame or praise. They themselves thought of the work they had done so far as being a strong springboard for their work in the future.

One evening in the library, shortly after publication of their book, Dr. Pirquet did something which was to have a tremendous effect on medicine in years to come. He invented a word.

"The word 'alteration,' " Béla was saying, "is scientifically correct but it is too vague. The body alters in other ways. I wish we could find a specific word for this specific alteration." As usual, he was sitting quietly at the table, while the high-strung Clemens was pacing up and down.

"I have been thinking of the same thing for quite a while. We want a word not yet in medical use, since the alteration we are describing has never been known." Dr. Pirquet went to the bookshelves and found a dictionary. "I think I know the word I want—a rare term and not in common usage. Here it is: 'allergy.' Its simplest meaning is: 'to react differently.' It fits our need. We can adopt it and give it the precise meaning of our discovery."

He could have no idea of the importance of what he had done. He could not then imagine that he had coined a word which was to become a familiar one throughout the world. Neither he nor Béla Shick had any idea then that they had put a name to what would become a separate and important part of medicine: the study of allergy and allergic diseases.

It is true that many years later allergy was to take on a slightly different meaning. The pathway which Dr. Pirquet and Dr. Schick had opened up for the world would make a sharp bend. Because the *symptoms* of the altered condition, the painful and distressing effects of the sharp reaction to proteins, would be so striking, allergy came to be the name for the symptoms rather than the cause. Doctors began to speak of a patient's *allergy* toward many different proteins. Diseases were named allergic diseases.

What Béla correctly called the hypersensitiveness—the extreme sensitivity of some patients toward the introduction of protein into their systems—was much later to be called the allergic reaction of patients.

But this was far in the future. In 1906 the two doctors only knew they had come across something highly valuable to medical knowledge.

They found that the students from the United States were especially eager to learn what they could about serum sickness and allergy. They learned about these new concepts directly from Dr. Schick, because he had had to take them as private pupils in order to stretch his tiny salary and be able to feed and clothe himself. He had never studied English in school so he taught himself out of books and by making his students correct him when he made mistakes. The Americans, whose university education in medicine was not up to the standard of Austria, were glad to have this special coaching to fill in the gaps of their knowledge.

Two of the students became good friends of his. One was Dr. Abraham Zingher and the other, Dr. Jerome Leopold, both of New York.

Of course, they had come to Vienna to study all the problems of children, not just serum sickness. They made the rounds with Dr. Pirquet and Dr. Schick. They attended lectures. They came to the masterful clinical demonstrations which Professor Escherich gave, in a small amphitheater where the students squirmed in discomfort on hard benches. At this weekly demonstration Dr. Escherich was always assisted by either Dr. Hamburger, Dr. von Reuss, Dr. Pirquet or Dr. Schick.

Since Escherich was remote and reserved and highly dignified, the young students sought out the assistants for social life. They found Dr. Pirquet to be more worldly than Dr. Schick;

in fact, they were inclined to think of Béla as an odd duck just at first. When they realized he simply couldn't afford parties and dances and the theater and coffee shops, they understood him better. When they came to know him, they fell under his gentle, humorous charm. To them, he was still unsophisticated and artless and candid and naïve, but a man of an unusually open heart.

The children knew this. They did not have to learn it slowly. They trusted Dr. Schick as children seldom trust grownups. They treated him as one of themselves.

While Dr. Pirquet and Dr. Schick went about their usual duties they were also moving ahead in their own research. Dr. Pirquet was particularly interested in following up their new understanding of allergy; he wanted to know what was happening to the body when it was vaccinated. He began to make observations of tuberculosis and of the tuberculin reaction.

Béla helped, but he was mostly concerned at the time with trying to understand everything he could about scarlet fever. Dr. Pirquet, and sometimes one of the other doctors, would work with him on some particular phase of it, but mostly he worked alone.

For two years he studied scarlet fever, explored its early symptoms, its course, immunity to it, and its terrible after-effects. He proved that many of those aftereffects were allergic in nature. He published one article after another on the subject of scarlet fever. By 1909, he had made one of the most exhaustive studies of this childhood disease that was ever made by one man.

Now he turned his attention to diphtheria.

In the meantime, in 1908, both he and Dr. Pirquet had moved up a step. Clemens became *Privatdocent* of the university and first assistant to Dr. Escherich; Béla became the second assistant.

At last he could move from his miserable room into a comfortable one inside the hospital, where he would get all his meals. However, since he was now living in and was the resident doctor, his salary stopped. It was lucky for him that he had his students or he would have had no cash in his pockets at all.

His father's grain business in Graz had failed completely, in spite of all the hard work he and Richard had put into it. The family had had to move to a nearby town where Jacques Schick still had some good business connections and where he and Richard could find work.

Béla wished he could help them, but he had hardly enough to keep his shoes repaired and his shirts mended. He had long forgotten what it was like to have the comfort of thick-soled, warm boots or a heavy overcoat.

That didn't bother him, because right now, ahead of him, lay the challenge of his fight against that deadly killer and crippler of children—diphtheria.

Every time he walked into the Diphtheria Pavilion his heart was wrenched with pity. Here lay a child who had been brought in, strangling from the ugly, gray membrane in its throat. That child was able to breathe only because Dr. Schick had managed to insert a tube into a cut he had made in the child's throat. The antitoxin was at work. Now he could only watch and hope that they had injected it in time.

Next to that child was a pretty little girl, convalescing from her attack of diphtheria. She would never run and play again. Her heart had been too badly damaged by the disease, even though her life was saved.

Another child nearby would be crippled as the result of disease.

Would the time ever come, Dr. Schick wondered, as he walked from bed to bed and soothed or talked or joked with each child, when diphtheria could be wiped from the face of the earth? He knew the bacillus, and he knew the poisonous toxin it gave off, and he knew the antitoxin which he could inject to help the body while it was manufacturing its own antitoxin.

If diphtheria struck only now and then—a child here and there—it might be possible to educate enough doctors to keep enough serum on hand to handle each separate case. Diphtheria, though, could become epidemic, and children in entire villages would be stricken.

Besides, arresting the disease after it started was not the answer. What was needed was some method of preventing diphtheria from spreading its toxin into every child.

The idea seemed impossible. Suppose you were to try to inject every child at the age of eight; there were millions of eight-year-old children in the world. It would be a gigantic task to get enough serum. Even then, the serum had to be cooked down, with time and patience and equipment. There weren't enough laboratory technicians or doctors to do it.

The parents, too, were a problem. Not all of them would agree to injections. They were superstitiously afraid of them.

Yet this great hope of preventing diphtheria stayed always in Dr. Schick's mind. He must do the same thorough research on diphtheria that he had done with scarlet fever. He must come to know it in every aspect and peculiarity and every pattern it took. Day after day, night after night, he studied and read, observed his diphtheria patients, carried out experiments in the laboratory on rabbits.

Dr. Pirquet had had the idea of making skin tests to see if a child had had a previous injection of serum, or if that child might have had a weak attack of a disease before. The skin test was a scratch with the needle, which just broke the skin enough for the new serum to enter. His theory was that, if the child did have antibodies in the system, there would be an immediate allergic swelling at the point of the scratch; if the child ever had had such antibodies and therefore the system was altered, was allergic, then the swelling would come very quickly.

The test worked fairly well with tuberculosis patients, though not well enough for Dr. Pirquet to feel he had proved his case completely. They tried it on diphtheria patients but here the test was a disappointment. They didn't know why, though they suspected that it had something to do with the fact that diphtheria was a disease of the toxins of the bacilli, not of the bacilli themselves.

Diphtheria was a strange disease. Its very strangeness, plus its killing wickedness, made Dr. Schick all the more determined to study it. On the other hand Dr. Pirquet was more interested in pursuing all sorts of allergic tests; he dropped the intense study of diphtheria.

Though they still worked together every day, it was not the close partnership of one single united interest as before.

All the while Dr. Schick was doing his other research into diphtheria, the lack of response and the strange behavior of the diphtheria skin test was like a question mark staring him in the face. It might not mean anything, but to every question mark there had to be an answer.

One day he thought: We were scratching into the skin the serum with antitoxin. Suppose the test were to be made with the toxin, instead? It was a strange thought because it was the reverse of what they had been doing. If he tried this, it would have nothing to do with allergy.

He had not just pulled this idea out of the air. It was the result of months—and now years—of patient study of diphtheria. He had forced himself to approach the problem of immunity in diphtheria from every angle, not just from the point of view of allergy.

This idea he now had was only one such angle, but he must experiment first on rabbits. He injected a small dose of antitoxin in one. Now it was as if the rabbit had either had a weak attack of diphtheria and his body had created antitoxins, or as if a doctor had given him an injection for immunity. These were the two possibilities that might happen to a child and make that child immune.

A few days later Dr. Schick cooked down a small quantity of the murderous toxin. He had to do it with infinite patience, slowly, carefully, until he had just the right amount which could not possibly *give* the disease to the rabbit. He scratched the skin of the rabbit with the sharp point of the needle, so that just the right amount went directly under the surface of the skin.

Nothing happened. There was absolutely no reaction that day nor any following day, as there should have been if this was an allergic response.

A few days later the man in charge of the laboratory brought in a new batch of rabbits, which had never before had injections of any kind. Dr. Schick was anxious to see what would happen to these, but first he had an inspiration. He would give the skin test to them.

The next day he found they all had red swellings at the place of the toxin scratch. Dr. Schick handled them and studied them. These rabbits had had no immunity; there were no antitoxins in their systems when he had given them that injection of diphtheria toxin to penetrate just under the skin.

Over and over, with skill and determination, he tested rabbits—those with antitoxins in them and those without. Always it was the same. Those without showed red swellings; those with immunity gave no physical response whatsoever.

What he was proving was so simple and yet had such great possibilities for the entire world that Dr. Schick forced himself to doubt and question it, make experiments over and over, without telling anyone. If he was right, then the skin test which would immediately tell which child was or was not immune to diphtheria was not an allergic test. It was simply this: that a scratch of the toxin was like the irritation of a very weak drop of acid. If the rabbit had antitoxin already in his system, it immediately neutralized the irritation of the toxin—destroyed it without any outward sign on the skin.

But if there was no antitoxin in the body, then the toxin caused a red, irritating inflammation. It was not enough to bring on the disease. It was just enough to warn that the body was not immune.

By the year 1910 Dr. Béla Schick was ready to experiment on a human being. He would try it first on himself. He had had previous injections of diphtheria serum. If his theory was right and all his experiments meant anything, then he should have no reaction to it whatsoever.

So it proved to be. He watched his arm but nothing happened. It would be harmless to try it on children and he must do so. He would give the toxin to those children in the Diphtheria Pavilion who he knew had had antitoxin in their systems; then he would give it to the little patients in the General Ward who might not.

The nurses were accustomed to his constant kind of research. They were anxious to help, because they knew by now that he would never experiment on a child if he thought there was the least danger. They knew all about the skin tests he had made with Dr. Pirquet, so that when he again scratched the skin of the diphtheria patients they were ready with sympathy.

"I'm sorry, Dr. Schick," they told him the next morning. "It was not successful. Like the last time, there is no sign of anything on the children's arms except just the roughness of the scratch."

They were surprised when he responded: "I am not disappointed, because I think that is as it should be."

They did not know that he was making the identical scratch test in the General Ward, where there were children who had heart troubles or bronchial troubles or small injuries, but no known cases of diphtheria. These were the children who would prove him right or wrong.

The next day he visited each of them in General. At least half had red swellings which gave them a little annoyance and discomfort. The rest showed the same smooth arms as did those in the Diphtheria Pavilion.

Carefully, while either cradling a child in his arms or pretending to caress a child's head and face, Dr. Schick managed to extract a tiny drop of blood from each earlobe. All that the children felt, if they noticed it at all, was the sensation of a pinprick in the ear.

Each precious drop was carefully put into a separate tube and labeled. Then Dr. Schick took them back to the laboratory and studied them under the microscope.

Half an hour later he knew he was right. He lifted his head from the eyepiece and let himself dare to hope and dream. It was a moment of the most intense rapture. There in front of him was the answer to the complete prevention of diphtheria anywhere—any time—on earth!

The children in the General Ward who had reacted with redness and swelling had no trace of antitoxin in their blood. It would be safe to say that they had never had the slightest natural invasion of diphtheria bacilli and toxin in their throats, to build up any immunity at all. Those whose blood showed antitoxin or antibodies had had no signs on their arms. Even though their charts, which would carry the reports the parents had made to the nurses, did not actually say that any of these children had once had diphtheria, they most certainly had had it. They had undoubtedly had such a weak brush with the diphtheria toxin that their mothers had dosed them for a bad cold.

Béla Schick had discussed all the other research on diphtheria with Dr. Pirquet, but not his skin test investigations. He had been too unsure of himself, until now, to risk a skeptical response.

Now, however, he was ready. In Dr. Pirquet's office he outlined every step, every deduction, every result. At first Clemens half listened; none of this was new. As Béla went on, his friend began to understand and he leaned forward intently so as to catch every single thought. ". . . and the result of all of this," finished Béla, "is that we have a practically foolproof method of easily and quickly and painlessly determining, among all children, which child is immune and which child is not. Instead of the impossible job of vaccinating every single child, we have only to find those who are not immune and vaccinate them."

The fire was beginning to glow in Dr. Pirquet's eyes, matching the eager confidence in Béla's. "A tiny scratch on the arm! That would tell us if a child were immune and safe, or not immune and therefore susceptible to an attack of diphtheria! But—" he checked his rising enthusiasm—"would the immunity last?"

"That is not important. We know that when a child begins to grow into adulthood he is out of danger. It is a childhood disease. If this year we could make the test on even seventy-five per cent of the children in Vienna, and repeat it the next year and the next, vaccinating every single one who shows what I call a 'positive' reaction, we could wipe out epidemics. Except in times of epidemics, only five to ten per cent of the children ever catch the disease. Gradually, through education of all doctors and parents, we could hope that they would cooperate with individual children." Béla's mind was seeing the future unfold.

"Eventually it might become the most natural and automatic thing for a doctor to ask every mother who brings a child to him, for whatever reason, if the child had the scratch test for diphtheria. If the child had not, then it would take one second to do it." Dr. Pirquet was becoming awed by the possibilities. "The genius of it, Béla, is that it is so simple. People are still ignorant and frightened of injections. On the other hand, parents dread the possibility of diphtheria striking their little ones. If parents thought that the test would show that the child did not have to have the injection, they might be eager for it."

He took off his glasses and wiped them carefully before putting them back on his nose. "You must write about this immediately! Do you need help? A volunteer? I wish I could work with you, but I have been offered the job of Professor of Children's Diseases at Breslau University, so we won't be able to see each other every day." He stood up and gripped Dr. Schick's shoulder. "You have found something of such importance I predict it will cause a storm of excitement in every medical journal in the world!"

7

Béla was not yet ready to write. The test was so simple and the results predicted so fantastic that he knew he had to compile a great many more test cases, over and over, so that his article would carry proof and weight.

In the meantime, in 1911, he was promoted to the place of *Privatdocent* of Childrens' Diseases of the University of Vienna. His best friend was delighted.

Hardly had Béla assumed all the new duties of his job when Professor Escherich died very suddenly. Béla felt a deep sorrow. He had admired and respected Escherich as he had come to realize how far in advance of his times he was, and how much he had already done to raise pediatrics to a valuable branch of medicine.

At his death, Dr. Pirquet was recalled from Breslau to take Professor Escherich's place at the university. He and Béla were at once faced with the gigantic job of finishing the new hospital which had only been started. Once again they were working together, although Dr. Pirquet's responsibilities were more and more administrative.

Upon their shoulders also fell the work of the old St. Anna Hospital; the compiling and writing up of their research in tuberculosis; all of the articles Béla must publish on his earlier

111

studies of diphtheria. Still he found time to go on making more
and more of the scratch tests and keeping the closest watch
on the results.

At last he knew there could be no possible doubt of what he
had discovered. He must write it for the widest possible cir-
culation. He wrote it at every odd moment: in the hospital
after rounds when the children were quiet and sleeping; in
the library, except that there he was always being interrupted
by an urgent call from a nurse; he even wrote it while on in-
spection in the nearly finished hospital, scratching away at his
notes while all around him workmen hammered and sawed
and talked to each other.

The hospital was finished before his article. Late in 1912
he and Dr. Pirquet had the bedridden children from St. Anna
carried over to new beds in the new hospital. Then they led
a parade of the nursing Sisters; all the children who could
walk, and the young doctor assistant, out of St. Anna and
down the street and around the corner to their new quarters.

Both Dr. Pirquet and Dr. Schick were very enthusiastic
about this new hospital. They had designed it for a maximum
of light and sun and air, with clean, bright rooms and plenty
of water piped in and lots of good gaslights for the evening.
To their surprise the children did not like it and some strongly
resented it.

The nurses, laughing, explained why. "They are so used to
the other and they felt cozy in its dark corners. It will take a
while for them to get used to so much light and air."

That made the doctors feel better. It was understandable
that children would like what was familiar to them and be
suspicious of change. They would gradually come to accept
the new hospital.

Béla had a special pleasure in it because there were two rooms—bedroom and sitting room—for himself. It was the first real home of his own he had ever had. He was getting a salary now. Since his father and brother were doing a little bit better and feeling it quite possible that they would be back in the grain business soon, he could afford at last to spend money on himself.

Characteristically, instead of new clothes he bought a piano.

With the hospital construction out of the way, he could now spend more time on writing. In 1913 he finished, not one, but five articles, each dealing with a different step in the process of his discovery—the most important one being "The Skin Reaction with Diphtheria Toxin on Human Beings as a Test Preceding the Prophylactic Injection of Diphtheria Serum."

It was a long and tongue-twisting title. No wonder that almost immediately the enthusiastic medical journals, plus all the doctors who wrote to him, shortened the whole thing and called it the "Schick" test. Dr. Pirquet was right: medical circles were startled and intrigued by the idea. Inquiries came from large hospitals in large cities, as far away as America. Praise was heaped on him. Inquiries were made of him, to find out just how to go about using the test on a wide scale.

Béla would not have been human if he weren't happy. Only a little of the happiness was for his own work; what thrilled him was the fact that this quick response might mean the quick use of the test.

By the late months of 1913, life seemed very good to Béla Schick. He had reason to expect that the Schick test would be a matter of discussion in medical papers all over the world. A few might oppose it. The majority of doctors, as eager as he to wipe out diphtheria, would test it for themselves and then champion it. After that, there would be only the problem of educating nations and families to understand how simple, how sure, how harmless the test was. Eventually it would be put into practice. There would be no more epidemics. Isolated cases of diphtheria could be caught quickly.

How anxiously and hopefully he dreamed that that "eventually" would be soon!

Meanwhile, his personal life had become richer. He had friends. In his sitting room he would occasionally take time to play duets with either Dr. Edmund Nobel or Dr. Wagner. Sometimes a chamber music quartette would meet in his room. Then the sound of his piano, another's violin, a cello and a viola would drift faintly downstairs into the children's wards. The children would turn in their sleep and smile.

He could afford to go to concerts and hear the music of his favorite Gustav Mahler, or to see a Puccini or Wagner opera. Béla had a trick which amused his friends. At the opera he liked the music, but sometimes not the looks of the singers. Then he would turn in his seat until he was facing sideways, close his eyes and hear only the glorious music.

The names of Dr. Béla Schick and Dr. Clemens Pirquet were rising stars in the field of pediatrics. Their work on serum sickness was becoming well known and appreciated. The students who came to Vienna took back with them glowing reports of their work. Pediatrics was a branch of medicine fast becoming respectable.

Most exciting of all, Béla was receiving letters from other doctors asking about the Schick test, complimenting him on it, wanting to discuss practical methods for applying it to whole towns and cities.

Then something happened which seemed to put an end to all of his hopes and dreams, threatening to bury, forgotten, his great discovery of the Schick test for diphtheria.

The World War of 1914 broke upon Dr. Béla Schick without warning. Suddenly, it seemed to him, everything changed. Instead of Strauss waltzes, the military bands drummed and bugled in the streets. Uniforms appeared everywhere.

Neither he nor Dr. Pirquet was the kind of superpatriot who would uphold his country, right or wrong. Austria and Germany had declared war, a war for power and with the aim of grabbing land from their neighbors. The doctors' sympathies were with the Allied nations of France and England and Belgium and the others.

"Isn't there enough suffering and misery in the world," exclaimed Dr. Pirquet savagely, "without adding the criminality of war?"

The foreign students went to their homes in their own nations. Doctors were called up to the Austrian military service. Fortunately, neither Dr. Schick nor Dr. Pirquet was taken, but it meant they were shorthanded at the hospital and must do the work of four or five men.

So much work tended to isolate them from the terrible war that was raging over Europe. Sometimes they heard the bands; sometimes they saw the uniforms; but their hospital did not take in wounded soldiers. They could concentrate on the children.

In spite of the extra work, Dr. Schick continued to add steadily to his knowledge of diphtheria, writing many articles on it. Dr. Pirquet's free time was devoted to research into the allergic reactions of tubercular patients.

Unfortunately, the war divided the medical world. When

Dr. Schick sent an article to an Austrian medical journal, proving that the Schick test would work, he had no idea whether that article would be picked up by a journal in any other country or if any doctors were reading it. At this moment in his life when he had accomplished a very great thing, it was rejected. He held out to the world a priceless gift of healing but the world was intent on killing, not healing.

There were other serious by-products of the war. Money from the Empire, which had formally gone to building up their pride in hospitals and universities, was diverted to making ammunition and guns. The Children's Hospital suffered. If a piece of equipment wore out, it was patched and patched until it had to be thrown away. Research became difficult.

By 1916, Béla and Clemens had to face the fact that the war was affecting their tiny patients. Cases of malnutrition due to lack of food began to come in. The war was not going well for Austria. More and more farmers were being called up for service; the women could not till the soil.

Hungry children, their bodies weakened, fell easy prey to disease. The beds in the wards were always full. The halls were overflowing daily with new cases. The Outpatients' Clinic was crowded; the mothers who came begged for milk even if their children had only a toothache.

The day came when the hospital kitchen had no fats, no lards or butter with which to cook. "We'll have to do without," Dr. Schick said to the cooks. "Be as careful as you can with all our supplies. They are dwindling away."

As 1917 came, with America entering the war, the people of Austria-Hungary knew that defeat was certain. It was. The year 1918 brought the signing of the peace treaty but it also brought the crumbling of the already-weakened Hapsburg monarchy and the Empire. Under the terms of armistice, Austria and Hungary were made into two nations. Austria had a republic, but the different parties and factions fought each other, and until matters could become more stable, the economy was a chaotic mess.

There were not enough raw materials or food. There were no markets yet for what little Austria did produce. Her government was doing its best to put in social reforms but there was little cooperation from businessmen or the former aristocracy.

So people starved. The doctors' first thought was: Feed the children! Keep them alive, somehow! It was an obsession that haunted Dr. Schick and Dr. Pirquet night and day. They scrounged for money everywhere they could. They went into the hospital kitchens and studied how the food was prepared and the amounts put into every dish for every child.

There was waste there. It was not intentional, but it was waste. Every mouthful was precious and it could not be wasted. A long line of mothers with children came every day for milk and bread; if Dr. Schick and Dr. Pirquet could save on what was given to the bed patients they would have more for the children outside.

By carefully judging the sitting height of a child, they were able to evaluate just exactly how much food he would rightfully require—down to the tiniest fraction of an ounce. They were scientific and accurate about it. They called their method N.E.M.—Nutrition Element Milk. Now they could give the cooks exact and mathematical formulas so that everything was weighed and nothing was spoiled or wasted. An enormous economy was instituted.

What was left over—together with what else they could

beg, borrow or demand—went to the starving children who came daily for their ration.

The American Red Cross began sending in parcels of food. Because it was known that Dr. Schick had been so clever in keeping the children fed, these parcels—all of them—were turned over to him for distribution in Vienna. Even other doctors in the city came to him for food for themselves and their own little patients.

Early one morning, after his own meager breakfast in the hospital, he went into the reception room where the parcels were distributed. Though it was not yet seven o'clock, a look out of the window showed him that the line was already forming. People waited patiently.

"Open the doors," Dr. Schick ordered. His volunteer helpers and nurses stood ready. He could hear the sighs, the whispers of gratitude, the voices outside which urged those behind not to shove, then the first mother and child stepped up to receive the life-giving parcel.

"Thank you, thank you," the old woman muttered, clutching it in her hands. The next woman, middle-aged, begged: "Herr Doctor, I have three children at home. May I have food for them, too?"

An assistant looked to Dr. Schick for approval, which she was sure he would give. But he shook his head. "We can give you milk for them. That is all."

"My children are hungry—" the woman said angrily "—and milk is not enough!"

"The others bring their children with them. I am sorry I cannot take your word for it that you do have these hungry ones at home," Béla answered her firmly, "but I cannot take chances even with one dishonest mother. There are too many people who would like to get their hands on extra parcels—to sell them. It is my responsibility to see that this food goes to those who need it, not to those who would make profit from it."

"The doctor is right! Bring your children, as we do!" shouted voices in line behind the woman.

After the last person left with the precious package of food and there was no longer a line, the exhausted nurses and helpers sank into chairs. One said to Dr. Schick: "Sometimes I think, Doctor, that you are too good to be human. You are a saint. After today, I know that you do sometimes see evil. You know it exists. Don't you ever become angry at evil? I am sure that woman had no children at home; there was something about her bold, demanding manner that was not like a woman pleading for hungry children."

"Why should I get angry?" he said gently. "We are all hungry. None of us has enough to eat. None of us has money. I can hardly blame someone, like her, for trying to make a few groschen, but I could not permit it," he flushed sternly. "It would be much more efficient if we could have many, many depots. There would not be such long lines waiting here. I would do it, except that I would have to put people in charge who might not be honest."

"I think," said another nurse, "that Austria should put up statues to you and Dr. Pirquet, instead of those silly statues of generals and kings who never did anything but get us into war."

Béla Schick threw back his head and laughed. "As if they would make a statue of me, you foolish girl! All I want is to know that people are fed."

Those around Béla loved and admired him for the sweetness

and goodness of his nature. They had never known him to do a mean or selfish thing.

Hungry, defeated people want to blame someone for their hunger and their shame. There were honest men in Austria who put the blame squarely where it belonged: on the insane ambitions of their former rulers. They called upon people to forget the past and work together for a republic which would give workers and farmers the right to choose their government.

Against these men were the dishonest ones, those who wanted to rise to power by way of human misery. They forced riots. They turned neighbor against neighbor. They cried out: hate the Slavs in Hungary—hate the English—hate the Jews and persecute them.

Dr. Béla Schick knew, vaguely, that such things were happening. His friend Clemens Pirquet knew a great deal more. He felt strongly that he should do something about it and go into politics.

In view of Dr. Béla Schick's most splendid record of service to the people of his country, neither of them had expected that the prejudice outside would strike inside, at Béla. But in that same year of 1918 the officials of the university informed him that he was now named *Extraordinary* Professor of Children's Diseases.

That *Extraordinary* was no honor; at best, it was a poor and shabby thing. Dr. Schick had for a long time been needed and wanted as a regular professor of the university. He had well earned that position. But because he was a Jew he could not have just the ordinary title. The "Extraordinary" must be tacked onto it, to set him apart from the others.

Dr. Pirquet was furious. There was nothing he could do but rage. "You are one of the foremost authorities in the whole world in children's diseases. The university is lucky to have you. You have done more for the university—for the whole of Austria—than they could hope to repay. How dare they do such a thing!"

Hurt as he was, Dr. Schick had not even been tempted to refuse the appointment. He was needed. That was all that was important. But he said, as the two men stood in the doorway looking at the classroom where next week Béla would start teaching, "What is happening to our whole country? I do not understand. Under the Hapsburgs I expected prejudice. I thought the attempt to set up a better government would result in better relationships between people."

"Good, decent people *are* trying, Béla. Most of the workers and most of the farmers are solidly behind social and economic progress, but those who were in power—the aristocratic land-owners—do not want to give up that power. They used to treat their farm workers like slaves. Then there are the men without work, without any intention of working. They are banding into lawless groups. Prejudice is a weapon in their hands. Béla, you should get out of the hospital more, to see what is going on."

With a flash of angry spirit, Béla replied: "I prefer the hospital. In the world of children there is no prejudice. Left alone, children would grow up to know no barriers among themselves. They sleep side by side in the hospital beds, chil-dren of all races and religions and nationalities. They play together. An ugly name for another child is just something they have heard from their elders."

Dr. Pirquet put his hand on the shoulder of his friend. Be-hind the eyeglasses he wore, his eyes softened and became affectionate. "I know. I only worry that there may be more trouble for you. I hate to think of you being so alone. Why don't you marry?" He himself had recently wed a lovely, frail girl, Maria, who adored him and was devoted to helping him.

"Me? No woman would have me." The twinkle was back in Béla's eyes.

"Don't tell me that. Every woman I know finds you attractive. The Sisters keep telling me to find you a good wife."

"I haven't the time, truly. Wouldn't you feel sorry for some poor woman who married me, when I spend all my time at the hospital? And now I'll be at the university, too." Smiling, Béla looked at his watch, closed the classroom door and set off for his next task at the hospital.

Letters from his mother, too, kept urging him to marry. She was always reminding him that Frieda was married to a Hungarian and already had a daughter, and Richard had at last found a wife.

Jacques Schick and Richard had saved money and reestablished themselves again in the grain business. They had moved back to Graz. Ilona was living at home. Béla saw little of any of them because feeding the children of Vienna was such an enormous job he had no time to travel. But in connection with his family he had a secret grief.

From his small salary, and from the little he received from the publication of his books and articles, he had—coin by coin—saved thirty thousand groschen, which before the war equaled around six thousand dollars. He had saved this in order to have a lump sum to give to his parents to help his father in business and insure comfort for his mother.

With the economic chaos of Austria had come such terrible inflation that all of Béla's thirty thousand groschen were worthless. They would buy exactly one dollar's worth of groceries, no more. All of his self-denial, going without things he needed or wanted, was for nothing. He grieved over it, only because he could not help his family.

As other doctors, now out of uniform, came back to the hospital, and as the economy of the country slowly improved so that there were only hungry people—not starving ones— Dr. Schick went back to his research. Dr. Pirquet was gone for long stretches of time. He was a representative to the League of Nation's committees on public health and preventative medicine. Béla worked alone.

It was difficult now. There was still no money for new medical equipment. The old was wearing out. Béla did not mind shabbiness or walls that needed paint; he did mind not having good tools to work with. Yet he persevered. He wrote articles on the allergic nature of asthma, eczema, vasorhinitis, urticaria, migraine and others—always insisting in his articles that Dr. Pirquet's name be recognized as the father of this new science of allergic medicine.

In 1922 he was forty-five. He had worked unceasingly since he was graduated from the Graz University, with scarcely a day of rest. Now it seemed to him that he was middle-aged and the progress of his work was slowing down for reasons he could not control.

Offers came to Dr. Pirquet, but not to Dr. Schick.

He went on, laboriously cooking his cultures in the old way, although he read of expensive new machines which could do it better. He worried because sheets and blankets which he needed for the children were wearing out. He taught his classes well, but even there he sometimes wondered if the dirty poison of anti-Semitism was not affecting some of his students.

The final insult was given him in a roundabout, shamefaced way. One of the officials of the university suggested to him that it was possible for a Jew to change his religion—then all obstacles in his path would be cleared away!

Béla pretended not to understand. He was both sickened and revolted. The man was proposing, without actually saying so, that Dr. Schick go through a ceremony of becoming either Catholic or Protestant. He would no longer then be an *Extraordinary* Professor. He could then be recommended highly to other hospitals who would be eager to have him.

It was utterly cynical. He was to pretend to be converted to another faith, just for ambition. Béla Schick was not a religious man but he was an honest one. He would not act in any way that would dishonor the heritage of his mother and father. He would not become apostate.

That afternoon, sore at heart, he left the hospital for a short while and walked through the streets of Vienna. At first he was scarcely aware of the scene or the people around him, so occupied was he with his thoughts.

Was it ambition that was frustrating him? No. He was the least ambitious of men. But pediatricians were so sorely needed in all hospitals. He was an expertly trained pediatrician, yet they did not want him.

He was near a famous coffee shop and his steps slowed. Without realizing it he was waiting for the gay, waltzing music he had heard coming from it on that first day he had walked through Vienna. Music there was, but it puzzled him. The people who went in and out of the coffee shop puzzled him, too.

What was it? He had to stop and go in, to find out. The noise was deafening. Everyone talked too much and too loudly. The women were overpainted. The men laughed too loudly, or argued among themselves, or quarreled with the waiters. There was a hectic, feverish quality in the air. Béla turned and went out.

The gay and thoughtless, gallant Viennese—what had happened to them?

Walking more slowly now, he observed more. He saw old women in alleys digging into garbage cans for food. He was approached by beggars. He came to a street corner where a large group had gathered around a speaker, who was crying out:

"We must unite, brothers, and make our own destiny! The war was not one we made, but one the monarchy made for its own ends. Now we are a republic. We must forget the past. Forget old hatreds and all work together for a peaceful solution to our problems. . . ."

A small stone hit his shoulder. A voice from the back of the crowd yelled: "Traitor!" Other voices took it up—"Traitor!" they cried. "We should have won the war—where is your patriotism? We were betrayed by those who made money at home—by the Hungarians—by the Jews—"

The rest of the crowd shifted uneasily and some moved forward to guard the speaker. In a second the group had split up into fiercely arguing knots of men, yelling at each other, with no one listening to the other. The threat of violence was over for the time being, but Béla felt it hanging in the air.

He went sadly back to the hospital. Here he found Clemens and told him what he had seen and heard.

"Béla, you are so wrapped up in your world of children that you have not been aware of much of what has been going on outside," Clemens Pirquet said to him. "It is right

that you should be; someone must. You haven't the temperament for politics. I, on the other hand, cannot stay out of it.
Austria will go one of two ways: either she will forget the
past, admit she was wrong in fighting the last war, accept the
peace treaty, and build a strong, democratic future of social
reform. Or else she will look for someone, something, to blame
for her troubles—a scapegoat to persecute and beat—and let
the evil-minded men take over."

"That is a terrible picture you paint," said Béla, who was
paying less attention to the words than to the fine-drawn face
of his friend. He wondered to himself if such a high-strung
individual had the temperament for politics, either.

A despondency settled upon Béla, but he kept his despair
to himself. He began and carried through a tremendous study
of jaundice, the disease of the liver cells which showed itself
outwardly in a yellowness of the skin in the newborn child.
He went on with his research into all diseases which afflict
children. In spite of his personal emotions, Dr. Schick kept to
a high, clear, steady resolve that his life should be dedicated
to the children, no matter what the difficulties.

Sometimes he was heartened by letters from his former
students. Both Dr. Abraham Zingher and Dr. Jerome Leopold,
in the United States, were doing well and they wrote that
pediatrics was not as despised in America as it had been. It
was beginning to be well thought of; other doctors were beginning to refer parents with children to pediatricians, instead
of trying to handle the cases themselves.

Dr. Schick had a few other correspondents: men in Berlin,
in Paris, in London, even strangers from New York. He was
thrilled by the way Dr. William H. Park, a bacteriologist in
New York, had grasped the great possibilities of the Schick

test. Dr. Park wrote that he could do nothing on a widespread scale as yet, but the time would come when city authorities and schools and parents would wake up to the fact that diphtheria could be conquered.

These letters—and the children—and his friendship with Dr. Pirquet were the bright spots in those dark days.

He could not possibly have known, in 1922, that his life was suddenly to change, just because of another letter. This letter was from a Mr. George Blumenthal, President of the Mount Sinai Hospital of New York City, asking if the writer of the letter might call upon Dr. Schick while he was in Austria.

Béla replied, in his tiny, cramped handwriting, that he would be delighted to see Mr. Blumenthal. The day came for the appointment. He waited in his office. To his surprise, Mr. Blumenthal was accompanied by another man, the Vice-President of Mount Sinai, Mr. Leo Arnstein.

8

The two gentlemen from the United States wasted no time. They came right to the point. Would Dr. Schick be interested in coming to New York, to be head of the Pediatrics Department of the Mount Sinai Hospital?

Béla looked at them in astonishment. "Why do you want me? How do you know my name?"

Their astonishment was greater even than his. Didn't this quiet, nice-looking man know that he was considered the foremost pediatrician in the world? Didn't he know that doctors did not speak of allergy without naming Dr. Schick and Dr. Pirquet as the founders of this new branch of medicine? Didn't he know that the Schick test for diphtheria had been the subject for fierce debate for years, and that now medical men in the United States were eager to try it out on a large-scale program?

Obviously, he did not know. Mr. Blumenthal looked into Béla Schick's blue, steadfast, innocent eyes and conceived at that moment the same tenderness for him which captured everyone who met him.

"We would be greatly honored, Dr. Schick, if you would consent to come," he said. "We are prepared to make what we think is a good offer. You will not be so busy that you won't have time for a lucrative private practice, but we hope that the salary of twelve thousand dollars a year will be sufficient until your private practice is established to bring you more, to match your income here."

Béla heard the figure but thought he must be mistaken. His mind could not grasp such wealth. He hurriedly tried to make the exchange of dollars into Austrian money; he arrived at such a stupendous figure that he was sure the whole thing was a mistake and he had heard incorrectly. Besides, it was not important.

"Tell me," he said cautiously, "about the hospital. How many wards for children? How many beds in each? What kind of facilities do you have for research?"

He listened and he marveled. It seemed impossible. He remembered the time when American students must come to Austrian medical schools and hospitals because their own were so primitive. Now it was all changed. America was now pushing forward, in long, swift strides, to hold a leading place as far as technical material, the most advanced equipment, and daring innovations in hospital methods were concerned.

Béla was impressed. He was told that Mount Sinai Hospital provided a building for the children, and that some of its windows faced the green loveliness of Central Park; that the building held at least one hundred beds; that there were many smaller rooms for segregating and studying different kinds of illnesses; that there were excellent laboratories and they had skilled laboratory technicians; there was an Outpatient Clinic. There was the Children's Health Class—

"What is that? What is a health class?" Béla interrupted.

Mr. Arnstein explained. It was a child-guidance clinic. It was mainly for the poor children of the city, and great stress was laid upon the fact that children of all races and national origins were encouraged to come. Here they taught the child and the mother the principles of health and sanitation. It was also a means of giving each child a thorough physical examination.

"An excellent idea. If you have men in your hospital who can plan such a program, why do you need me? You must have good pediatricians of your own," said Béla.

"Because we want the best man." The answer came bluntly. "*You* are the best man, Dr. Schick."

They finally persuaded him to come on a visit to the United States and then make up his mind. After they left he sat staring into space, hardly able to believe this had happened, scarcely able to comprehend what it would mean.

It would mean leaving Vienna and Austria, his family and his friends and his closest fellow worker, Dr. Pirquet. He would be leaving this hospital and university, into which he had poured heart and soul.

He got up, automatically reaching for his white doctor's linen coat and putting it on. He walked out into the hallways. A nurse passed him, saying, "Dr. Schick, there's a new patient in the Scarlet Fever Ward. I do hope the poor little thing doesn't break out with serum sickness. She hasn't much strength to fight the disease as it is. She's nothing but skin and bones."

His heart gave a wrench. The nurse felt so free to talk to him. Would another doctor in his place here make them feel part of the medical teamwork, as he had always insisted upon doing? Another Sister, clucking her tongue, came up to him and rebuttoned his white coat. "You always button it wrong," she scolded. "You have your mind on so many things you don't pay any attention to what you are doing."

She was a particular favorite of his, a woman of rare intelligence. He admired women and thought them the equal of men. If he had had his way, any of these nurses who wanted to could have become doctors.

He was reminded that in Austria it was difficult. Would America treat women as equals? Would he have clever women doctors to train?

As he made his way to the wards everything he saw or touched had memories for him. There in those great cupboards they had stored the food packages which had saved so many Viennese lives. There in the library he and Dr. Pirquet had met so many evenings to read and discuss. He stopped in the doorway and saw it with fresh eyes.

It was not the library it had once been. From long handling the books, which had been their pride, were worn. There was almost no money for new ones. Instead of the great pile of medical journals on the table, they could afford only a few.

Sadly he turned away. The library at Mount Sinai Hospital would furnish him with that contact with other minds, which he so sorely needed.

He couldn't bear to go into the laboratory rooms which reminded him each time how badly they needed new equipment. What they had was patched and repaired. According to Mr. Blumenthal the hospital equipment at Mount Sinai would enable Dr. Schick to branch out into all kinds of new experiments.

In the Scarlet Fever Ward he thought: How can I leave them? But as he stood by the bedside of a pixielike little girl of eight, who had become a special pet of his, she said to him:

"Tomorrow I go home, Doctor!"

"Do you want to leave me, Elsa? Haven't we had fun together?" He sat down on the chair beside her bed.

"You are teasing me. I have to go home. You know that, Doctor." she said. After a second's thought, she peered shrewdly up at him. "All your children go home, don't they? You have new children all the time. How funny!"

Yes, he had new children all the time. The children came when they were sick. They went home when they were well. His love was not for any one child, but for all those who needed him. Didn't the children in America need him as much as these in Vienna? He would not be deserting. He would be stepping from a child's bedside in Vienna to one in America.

"Thank you." He bent and kissed Elsa.

"Why? What did I do?" she asked.

"You helped me make up my mind. I may go away, Elsa, to another country and another hospital, where they speak a different language—but the children will be the same."

She was alarmed. "You won't forget me?" When he shook his head she was comforted, but curious. "How can you talk to those children if you don't know their language?"

"Oh, I speak it very well," he boasted. It was one of the few, and very human, small conceits that Dr. Schick had. He thought his English very good; he was to find Americans very puzzled at first over his accent.

Dr. Pirquet was overjoyed when he heard the news. He urged Béla to accept.

They talked together one evening in Béla's simple but comfortable sitting room at the hospital. Dr. Pirquet walked about but Béla remained at the piano stool, striking a chord on its keys now and then, or playing a few bars of melody.

"You must go," said Clemens, "because you are wasted here. Think of the influence you can have on the young doctors of America, to say nothing of your own studies. But even if you have every fancy gadget and all the beautiful equipment in the world, will you ever forget how proud we were of our new hospital when it was first built?"

Dr. Schick smiled. "Remember how the patients thought it was too clean and bright and too big—and how they wanted to go back to the old St. Anna?"

"Neither of us will ever forget the St. Anna. The nights we used to spend, going from bed to bed with our candles to see if our little ones had broken out with serum sickness!" Clemens' fine eyes were clouded with the happiness of memory and the sadness of nostalgia. "You will have the best of electric lights at Mount Sinai, but it won't tell you anything more than our candles when we looked at little Egon."

"I haven't accepted the offer yet," protested Béla. "I am only going to look at America and the hospital." He played a slow melody and then a few bars of a gay tune. He laughed. "Do you remember the boy who insisted that the hives were little animals biting him and who was so shocked that the hospital would have fleas?"

They reminisced for the rest of the evening. They were grown men and only in this way could they express to each other the fear and the sadness that their partnership might be breaking up.

As Dr. Pirquet finally rose to go, Béla asked the question which had been bothering him. "And what of you, Clemens? Can you go on working here?"

"I think so. I believe there is a good chance for promoting social health programs. I will have to work with all kinds of people—honest ones and dishonest ones—but the *von* still commands some respect." He said it scornfully.

"Take care of yourself, all the same. I wish you would stick to medicine, where you are a professional. In this political and economic struggle, you are an amateur, Clemens. You know the fate of amateurs; you will be kicked by all sides." This was as much warning as Béla could give his dear, though headstrong, friend.

Dr. Schick was making his preparations to leave for the visit to America. Letters began pouring in from his former American students, with all kinds of plans for him. Letters came from strangers, asking him to speak at medical affairs, to preside at functions, to attend receptions. He was bewildered. He did accept the invitation from Harvard University, to give the famous Cutter Lectures there.

At this moment came sad news from Graz. Jacques Schick had died suddenly. Just when things were looking much brighter for the family, the father had died. He was seventy-four years old.

Béla went to Graz immediately. He sorrowed for his father, but more for his mother. Jacques Schick had had a rich, full life. He was a popular man. He had seen his children grow up to be respected and happy. But what would his mother do now? Béla almost felt that he should not go to America.

After the funeral, he talked to Richard who was emphatic that Béla must go. "We are proud of you and we know how hard you work. Even when you are in Vienna we do not expect to see much of you, because we know it is impossible. Serena is here in Graz and Frieda is not too far to visit. I will stay at least for a while, and Ilona is living with Mamma. You must go, Béla."

He would not agree until he had spoken to each of his sisters and knew they were willing. He insisted that he would send back money for his mother's support every month, if he decided to stay in America.

Then he took his farewell of his mother. She seemed, to his eyes, to be as lovely as ever; indeed, her years had only added dignity. He embraced her and she whispered: "Promise me you will get married to some nice American girl?"

Béla laughed. Always the same! "I am forty-five, Mamma. You are my only girl."

In January of 1923 he sailed for New York. The ship docked in what seemed to him a whirl of noise and confusion of baggage handlers, porters and custom men. Out of this bedlam he was plucked by a distinguished group of men— leading doctors of New York who were the welcoming committee. No sooner did they leave the dock than it seemed to him he was in worse confusion. So many motor cars! So many hurrying, busy people on the streets.

Taxis honked. Newsboys shouted. High up on the fourteenth story of a skyscraper being erected came the machine-gun rattle of the riveters. On the river the huge boats added their hootings. It was a discordant symphony, but as soon as Béla had caught his breath he found he liked it.

What he didn't like was being treated with awe, as a celebrity. For that reason he was overjoyed that both of his students, Dr. Abraham Zingher and Dr. Jerome Leopold, had come to the docks with the delegation and that they stayed in the taxi with him.

"It is wonderful to see you again, Dr. Schick—" Dr. Zingher started to say.

Béla interrupted him. "Why do you call me that? Have you forgotten how to say 'Béla'? *Bay*-la," he pronounced it slowly, and they all laughed. The atmosphere was eased and they chatted about the old days in Vienna and the new days in America. He caught from both these former students of his a sense of progress and excitement and impatience for scrapping the old and building the new, which he was to find characteristic of New York.

In the days that followed there were many things he didn't like. He felt that Americans grabbed for a novelty without truly considering its worth. He found a lack of appreciation for what Europe had contributed. But he shed completely the despondency of the past few years in Vienna.

He liked the fast tempo; so much so, that sometimes he had to dig his heels in to escape being carried away by it. He would not yet agree to be the permanent head of the Mount Sinai Pediatrics division.

Medical societies begged him to speak at their meetings. Conferences were arranged for him. The pediatric heads of universities and hospitals all wanted the renowned and distinguished Dr. Béla Schick to come and visit their departments. He gave the Cutter Lectures on "The Prevention and Control of Diphtheria" and was given a standing ovation at the end of his talks.

For the first time he realized that important medical men considered his Schick test for diphtheria one of the great advances in the control of disease. They considered it practical and were eager to put it into effect. They spoke of him as the genius who had taken the final step toward forever wiping diphtheria from the face of the earth.

Alone in his hotel room, Béla Schick felt overwhelmed. He was not proud of himself. He was humbly grateful that he had had the opportunity to make the discovery, and humbly glad that it had not been forgotten or overlooked.

Whenever he was praised for his pioneer work in allergy, he quickly and fiercely responded by insisting that Dr. Pirquet be given the credit. Doctors listened to him and smiled. They knew the partnership of ideas and creation between the two men.

Over a period of several years Béla had been in correspondence with Dr. William H. Park, who was now Chief of the Bureau of Laboratories of the Department of Health of the city. It was a big title but that was all right—Dr. Park was a man of big ideas. When they met at last, Dr. Park got right down to business.

"We hope someday," he said, "to give the Schick test to all the children of New York. We've already begun in a small way but the publicity over your coming here—"

"I'm not sure I am coming back," Béla objected.

"Oh, you must. The publicity, and your name, will help us tremendously. We can win over the whole medical profession and then the authorities and then the parents. It will take time but I predict, Dr. Schick, that there will come a day when children will grow up in this country without any fear whatsoever of diphtheria," declared Dr. Park.

Béla listened to him and the old, rapturous dream began to flower again in his heart. No more diphtheria! . . . no more watching children strangle . . . no more putting tubes into their throats so they could breathe . . . no more watching those who recovered spend the rest of their lives as cripples. *No more deaths.*

If America produced the men who could launch such a campaign, then he should be with them, to help them.

There were other inducements to come back and stay. He made real friends. Dr. Zingher invited him to a reception at his home. There Béla met charming people and among them a young woman, Margaret Fries: smart, intelligent, attractive *and* she was a pediatrician. He was aware, and amused, that the other guests left him alone with Margaret, hoping for a romance.

He did like her. She was capable and determined about her profession. She told him about herself and her family. Her father, Albert Fries, was a well-to-do real estate broker who had sent both her sister, Cathy, and herself to the university.

"Is your sister also a pediatrician?" Béla asked.

"Cathy? Oh, no, she studied law and is practicing now, but I am afraid Cathy is not serious enough about her work to make a real career out of it."

When it was time for Bela to leave New York, only one voice spoke out against his returning. Dr. Jerome Leopold was worried that Dr. Schick would find the change far more difficult than he realized. "You won't like it," he warned. "The pace is too much faster than in Vienna; there is not the informality among doctors, which you are accustomed to. Ambition and power and hospital inner politics—those are the things you will run into and you will hate them."

Béla Schick had no concept of such things in the medical profession and he only smiled and thanked Dr. Leopold. The real question for him was the tearing up of all his roots and the deep love he had for his own people and his native land. Could he do it?

When he reached Vienna he told his worries to Dr. Pirquet. The two had met with the same gladness, but already there was a difference in their relationship. The breakup of partnership had come, whether they willed it or not.

Clemens Pirquet was vehemently insistent that his friend make a final decision to work at Mount Sinai. "You will rot here. It is your duty to go. You liked it, didn't you? Then why not?"

"Jerome Leopold said I would never be at home in New York. He said I would be homesick for Vienna," answered Béla.

"For the old Vienna that he knew, yes. You will not be homesick for what it has become. How is Jerome doing? What else did he say?"

Béla replied, "Jerome has done very well. We can be proud of him. He has made a most important contribution to the feeding formulas for infants." Then Béla said, in a bewildered way, "One of the reasons he thought I might not like New York was that the Americans would not be able to understand me. But I speak good English! He said I might have trouble directing a taxicab driver, but I never take taxis. I walk."

Dr. Pirquet laughed fondly at his indignant friend. "What other reasons are there for your not going back?"

"The examination. All foreign doctors must pass an examination to practice medicine in the United States. It is in English. I think I speak well enough, but I might have trouble understanding extremely technical, scientific words if written in English. Everyone assured me the matter could be arranged. I hope so."

"I hope so, too. I think you want to go, Béla. It is right that you should go." Dr. Pirquet said it with finality. "Besides, I have a surprise for you. We can travel together. I have accepted a short-term teaching engagement—for a few months —at the University of Minnesota's Department of Pediatrics."

Then the heart of Dr. Schick felt light. Their separation had been postponed.

Letters from prominent medical men and public officials of the state of New York came to him in Vienna, assuring him that he would never have to take that examination. They were sure of it. There was only one Dr. Béla Schick in the world and the United States was not going to lose the chance to have him as an adopted son.

His mind was at last made up, in spite of his dread of that test in English. He worried about it, but he was hopeful that the letters meant what they were saying. He spent a few days in Graz saying farewell, promising to write and come back for as many visits to his mother as he could. He packed his few personal belongings, sold his piano, arranged to have his books shipped. Then he was ready.

It was with a strange feeling of excitement for the future and nostalgia for what he was leaving that he boarded the train with Dr. Pirquet. By the time they were on shipboard they were having such a rare and pleasant vacation, he had no time to brood over the hospital in Vienna.

They landed in New York on September 30, 1923. From that moment on, as Dr. Béla Schick put foot on American soil, he was rarely known to look back. He was as eager for the future as any young boy.

Again Dr. Leopold was waiting to meet him. They journeyed uptown to a modestly priced hotel, which suited Béla perfectly. "You will have to have a place to live," Dr. Leopold told him. "There are no living quarters for you at the hospital. Would you like me to find a place for you?"

"Yes, please, Jerome; some place small and clean, but cheap. I cannot pay a high rent," Béla reminded him.

"You will have to have an office for your private practice. I'll try to find an apartment large enough for you and for an office," said Dr. Leopold.

"Nonsense, I won't have time for that. I will be too busy all day long at the hospital." Béla was firm and the matter was dropped.

One day of taking care of urgent business matters, writing letters home, telephoning a few friends that he was in New York to stay, saying good-by to Dr. Pirquet—and the holiday was over. The next morning, bright and early, Dr. Schick presented himself at the doors of the imposing stone building that was Mount Sinai Hospital.

The receptionist was flustered. "Dr. Schick? I don't think they are expecting you so early!"

"That is all right. I think I remember the way to the wards. I can go by myself." He smiled at her.

He did find his way to the office of Dr. Herman Schwartz who had been acting as head until Béla's arrival. Béla did not know it then, but Dr. Schwartz had fully expected to be made official head and was not happy that he had been superseded. He was a very capable pediatrician. It was only natural that for some months to come—until he, too, fell under the spell of Dr. Schick's charm—he would be jealous and a bit uncooperative.

"Would you like to make yourself at home here in your office first?" asked Dr. Schwartz.

"Later, later; there is plenty of time for that. You were about to make the rounds of the wards, yes? I should like to go with you. I want to see the children." Béla ached to see the children. He had been away from them too long.

As they walked out of the office Dr. Schwartz made polite conversation. "It is a nice day. Did you have a pleasant ride to the hospital from your hotel?"

"I did not ride. I walked—"

"Walked?" Dr. Schwartz was astonished. "Why?"

"I walk whenever I can. And I saved ten cents of your money—that would buy a loaf of bread in Vienna," he explained.

That remark made the rounds of rumor all through the hospital by the end of the day. It scandalized some and amused others. What kind of a queer bird was this famous doctor who earned a good salary at Mount Sinai; who could earn fabulous sums in private practice, but who walked to save the price of a loaf of bread?

They had not gone hungry as Béla had. They had not had to feed starving thousands and see others turned away because there was not the price of a loaf of bread.

Meanwhile the two men went into the first Children's Ward. Here were the children. Béla wondered if they would like him. Perhaps, at first, they might think he talked in a strange way.

He bent over the first child, a tiny boy with great dark eyes. As he did so, Béla could almost feel the terrible fear emanating from the child. "Are you frightened, little one?" he asked, putting a hand on the boy's forehead. "Why? We are good people. We are here to make you feel better."

He realized that the boy's eyes, which had been clinging to

his, had shifted to the nurse who was approaching with an injection needle. She handed it to Dr. Schwartz.

"Is this little patient new in the hospital?" Béla asked.

"He was just admitted an hour ago," replied the nurse.

"Ah, I see." Béla sat down beside the bed and held the boy's hands in his. He addressed himself to the child, so it would not seem that he was reproving either the nurse or the other doctor. "And you don't understand yet about all the things we do here, do you? We put funny little flat sticks on top of your tongue and we ask you to open your mouth wide, and it frightens you because you don't understand. But it didn't hurt you, did it? Now, why don't you just lie here quietly and look around you and talk to the little boy in the bed next to yours—and get acquainted with us? We won't do anything more to you for a while."

"No injection?" asked Dr. Schwartz.

"I think it is better that we wait until this boy decides we are his friends." He patted the little hand and tried to disengage himself, but the child clung to him. Dr. Schick understood and he stayed and talked until the big dark eyes were no longer frightened. He knew that he was upsetting the ward's visiting routine but one child was more important than hospital efficiency.

The young interns had gathered around and were introduced. Among them was Dr. Samuel Karelitz, twenty-three years old. As the ward visits were resumed, with the interns trailing along, Dr. Schick spoke to Dr. Karelitz.

"I remember your name. Dr. Park spoke to me of you— very highly. You are to be my resident pediatrician?"

"Yes, Dr. Schick." As resident, Samuel Karelitz would have a room at the hospital.

"Then we shall see a lot of each other. Don't be surprised if I wander in late at night or early in the morning. I am accustomed to living in a hospital and I cannot break old habits," Dr. Schick told him.

From bed to bed they went, as Dr. Schwartz gave a summary of each patient. The time was getting late. No one had expected that Dr. Schick would hang around for the afternoon hours. They were his "free" time, when it was taken for granted that he would be out establishing his private office and accepting his first private patients.

Instead, Dr. Schick poked his head into everything. He asked every nurse what she was doing, what her name was and how long she had been at the hospital. He wanted to see the kitchens and meet the cooks. He examined every piece of laboratory and testing equipment, exclaiming over the bright new, modern machines.

When everyone else was exhausted he was still fresh and still going on. "Where is your Outpatient Department? I visited it when I was here before, but I do not remember just where it is," he asked.

Reluctant and annoyed, Dr. Schwartz led the way downstairs where they visited several rooms. Here came the poor of the city for the treatment of eyes and throats and minor ailments. They came to the open door of another room and Béla peered in, to see a young man doing something mysterious to the arm of a small girl.

He looked inquiringly at his guide, so Dr. Schwartz introduced him to the young man. "This is Dr. Murray Peshkin, Dr. Schick. We let him use this room. He is devoting full time to that new fad—allergy." This was tactless of him, seeing that Dr. Schick was a pioneer in allergic studies. Having said this, he firmly took hold of Dr. Schick's arm to lead him away.

"Wait a moment, there is something here that I wish to see and to know more about," said Dr. Schick, releasing himself with dignity from Dr. Schwartz's hand. Though it had all happened quickly, there had been an unspoken clash of wills between these two men. Now it was plain that, for all his gentle kindness, Dr. Schick was not to be pushed around.

"What are you doing?" he asked young Murray Peshkin.

"Skin tests for allergy," Dr. Peshkin answered rudely. He was a fiery man, because he had had to fight for time to do what he wanted, and fight for space and permission for his research, against the contempt of older doctors. Since Dr. Schick continued to look at him with patience and understanding, Dr. Peshkin relaxed and his manner became more friendly.

"This child," he explained, "has a constant runny nose and swollen eyes. I think she is allergic to some common, ordinary substance in her own home and I am testing out all kinds of things—dust, feathers, even furniture polish. By injecting a tiny amount of the protein I can see from the welt if she is allergic or not."

Dr. Schick was fascinated. This was a great new path of exploration for allergy. He and Dr. Pirquet had worked with the allergic changes in infectious diseases, after injections. Here was a young man who was testing out hypersensitiveness of the human organism to all kinds of proteins.

If Dr. Schick had been a conceited man, he might have objected to the use Dr. Peshkin made of the word "allergy." He had noted the same change in the word, in some articles in medical journals. Originally, he and Dr. Pirquet had called the altered nature "allergy" and the rash and swelling and fever were the hypersensitive reaction to that alteration. More and more, however, scientists and researchers had slid into the habit of calling the symptoms "allergy."

It was not important. What was important was that such a young man as this one should be using his brain to try to understand the peculiar sensitivity of some individuals to some proteins. Béla Schick lingered in the room, asking alert questions, giving encouragement and appreciation, and sympathizing with Dr. Peshkin that this one little room was inadequate for clinical research.

By the time he at last yielded to Dr. Schwartz's urgings and proceeded to the other rooms, he had left behind him a much-stunned young man. Dr. Peshkin could hardly believe it. The new head of the Pediatrics Department had faith in him and what he was doing. From that moment on, Dr. Peshkin was almost to worship Dr. Schick.

Nor was this first meeting the end of it. In the months to come Dr. Schick gave all the help he could, to set up a real allergy clinic. He was a constant visitor to Dr. Peshkin's department. He brought his staff down there and saw that they were instructed in the nature of allergies. He told Dr. Peshkin: "I recognize as my allergist only you," even when others became interested in the research.

From the second day of Dr. Schick's role as head, he insisted that the interns and doctors who labored in the Outpatients' Department be allowed to come up and make the regular rounds of bed visits with the rest of the staff. This had never been done before.

He also instituted the clinical demonstration, to which all the staff members were invited. Usually it was Dr. Schick who stood by the side of the patient, giving diagnosis and discussion and treatment and then opening the meeting for any questions. These demonstrations became so popular and were visited by so many doctors from other hospitals that, in time, they had to be moved to a special auditorium. Whenever possible, at these meetings, he asked young members of his staff to make the demonstration, with his help.

9

Long before he actually came to Mount Sinai, the staff and the interns had speculated what kind of man this Austrian would be. They feared a brisk, a whirlwind, a domineering kind of man who would sweep through the department, ordering people about right and left.

They found he was totally unlike what they had imagined. He did make changes, but in a kindly manner. He looked for the good in every nurse and doctor—and found it. They realized he liked order and routine, but also a relaxed attitude in the wards. He felt it was good for the children.

This, everyone soon realized, was the pivot on which Dr. Schick's life rested and turned. Was it good for the children? Nothing else really mattered much.

The most remarkable change was that, unlike the other heads who had preceded him, Dr. Schick seemed to be always in the department. He refused to stay in his apartment, to build up a wealthy private practice. So whenever a nurse or a young doctor ran into a problem there was Dr. Schick, within call or right at the bedside.

Doctors in New York did ask him to handle special patients of theirs when it was a particularly difficult case. Dr. Schick would receive them in his basement apartment, unaware that they were shocked at the humble rooms. Dr. Leopold had found just the place which he knew Dr. Schick would like, on East Eighty-fourth Street. It was considered unsuitable for a famous man . . . two rooms and bath, in a basement! . . . for a doctor in his position, it was unbelievable.

They could not know how pleased Béla was with them. They made him feel at home, where he would have been lost in something larger and more magnificent. He even felt that soon he could put in a piano and then he could invite some friends.

The acquaintances he had made on his first visit were fast becoming close friends. He was invited often to the home of his former student, Dr. Abraham Zingher, and there he met again Margaret Fries. Béla liked her. He was delighted that so intelligent a young woman should be a pediatrician like himself.

So when she asked him to come to her home for a dinner party, he went with pleasure. He was now forty-six years old. He had given up any idea of marrying—but, oddly enough, the novelty of his life in America, with its radical changes, made him feel dissatisfied with his lonely, bachelor existence.

That evening he found Margaret's parents congenial, cultured people, whose luxurious apartment reflected their good taste. Béla approved of them. He liked the fact that they had insisted upon careers for their daughters, even though there was no financial need for them to work.

Then Cathy walked into the living room. He had not met this younger daughter. His first thought was that he *should* not like her, as he did Margaret. Margaret was serious-minded; Cathy was lively, gay, even flippant. By the standards of Viennese ladies he had known, who were willowy, languid creatures, this Cathy Fries should not have appealed to him. She didn't languish or droop. She was so full of life she moved with dramatic zest. Béla was accustomed to nurses in uniform, or career women in dark, businesslike suits; Cathy liked vivid colors. The red dress she had on was particularly becoming to her.

She wore her hair short. She was tall and she moved with a coltish grace. She made Béla laugh before they had been together two minutes.

"So you are Margaret's sister?" he asked.

"How would you like to be known just as someone's sister, or brother? I'm Cathy. And you are the famous Dr. Schick. I wear your name above my heart."

Before he could properly draw back at this immodestly forward maiden, she showed him what she meant. It was a blue and white button which stated boldly: "I am Schicked. Are You?"

Béla laughed then. He knew what the button was; he had been given one, too. It came from the Boston Health Department and it meant that the wearer of the button had been given the Schick test. It was an endeavour to popularize the test and give it widespread publicity.

"Cathy!" remonstrated her mother. "You will embarrass our guest."

Cathy had meant to tease him. She had thought, from her sister's description, that he would be a very proper, very grave man, fully aware of how important he was. Now that she saw the twinkle in Béla's eye, and when she heard him compliment her dress because red was his favorite color, she felt very differently about him.

When he left the Fries apartment that evening and walked to his own, he could not get Cathy out of his mind. Not that he was in love!—he scoffed at the idea. He was sixteen years older than she was. She was much too modern, too breezy, for his old-fashioned ways.

Yet the city streets seemed beautiful to him that evening. His heart was strangely lifted. Old, tender, sentimental love songs kept coming back to him and he hummed them as he walked.

For a month, while he was extremely busy, he saw nothing of her. Then he was again invited to her home and she was there. He found himself wondering if she would be, since his invitation came from Margaret. In fact, he and Margaret were now working together on writing a paper on "Observation of the Nutritional Effect of Subcutaneous Oil Injections."

But if Margaret had thought to engage the great Dr. Schick in a weighty discussion of subcutaneous oil injections, Cathy had other ideas. She wanted to talk about music and the theater. Béla enjoyed listening to her and arguing with her. He liked to look at her, seeing the quick expressions chase themselves across her lively face as she talked.

Above all things, he found he loved to laugh with Cathy Fries. He had always had a sense of humor, but it was repressed. He used his wit in a gentle way, usually, to point up a lesson for students, and sometimes he would tell a little joke and chuckle. But with Cathy he learned the great joy of laughing out loud at an exchange of pure nonsense.

It did not escape his eyes that she was still wearing the button with his name on it.

She mentioned a particular art museum. What was more

natural, several days later, than that he should feel impelled
to visit that museum and that Cathy Fries should just happen
to be there?

It was a long, long time, almost a year, before he actually
asked her to to go to dinner with him. It had seemed so unbelievable to him that she would continue to like him; he had
waited to make sure.

They went to an unpretentious, inexpensive Hungarian res-
taurant which he had found. They talked about themselves.
He found that, for all her gaiety, she had a keen mind. She
was in a law office and would have made a good career out of
it, except that she was much too interested in people, the
theater, good art and music, dogs—and in Béla Schick, although he could not be sure of that yet.

He tried to be honest with her. He told her how different
his life had been from hers. "I've always lived just for medicine. I don't know anything else, except music. I'm afraid you
will find me a dull, stodgy, quiet sort of man."

"For such a dull man you seem to stir up plenty of excitement," she said. "And for such a stodgy man, you seem to
have plenty of attractions. Margaret tells me you have a harem
of women at Mount Sinai."

"My harem." Béla's eyes were still a bright, bright blue and
now they twinkled behind his glasses. "They call themselves
my harem. They are wonderful young women doctors and I
try to help them."

"You help everyone," said Cathy. She was thinking: *But
who helps you and looks after you?*

In her impetuous but clear-sighted way, she knew she
wanted to be the one to look after Béla Schick. She knew

she was in love, but she was content to wait. If Béla wanted to keep their courtship a lovely secret—if he was shy in expressing his emotions, she could wait.

He was not only shy but bewildered. He could not believe he was falling in love. How could he fit marriage into his life?

If Cathy had not been so easy and relaxed and natural to be with, he would probably have run away from this romance as he had carefully skirted away from all others. The remarkable thing to him was that for all of Cathy's high spirits, there was no strain or tension when he was with her.

A year went by. Now it seemed to him that she was becoming such a part of his life he could not imagine it without her. She adapted her time to his. She never complained because he was too busy to see her.

There was certainly plenty to keep him occupied. Administering such a large pediatric department in such a large hospital forced him to change his methods of research. He went steadily ahead on his own, but not to the same degree as before. Instead he pushed others, made suggestions to others, encouraged them and helped them in their research.

His young assistants and interns were scared of him at first. They knew he had discovered the Schick test. They knew that it was the subject of great argument, debate and publicity in the American medical world; that it was slowly gaining approval.

They knew their head of pediatrics had been singularly honored by the state of New York. Two months after his arrival he had received a letter from the Assistant Commissioner and Director of Professional Education of New York State. It read:

My dear Dr. Schick:

I have pleasure in advising you that the Board of Regents, at a meeting held November 15, 1923, formally voted to grant you a medical license on approval, because of the eminence and authority which you have attained in your profession.

May I ask you to forward to me at your earliest convenience the original diploma granted you by the University of Graz. In accordance with the statute, this is the document which will be endorsed as a license to practice medicine in this state.

Very sincerely yours,
August S. Downing

So Dr. Schick did not have to take the dread examination in English. This special permission was so rare that no one had ever heard of such a thing; only four or five other famous doctors since then have been permitted to practice with just a diploma from a European university.

It was natural that his staff would be in awe of him. He was a celebrity. What they soon found out, however, was that Dr. Schick didn't know he was a celebrity, didn't act like one, and gave these young people the same compassionate, thoughtful help he would have wanted for himself.

He soon realized that America's treatment of women doctors was no better than Austria's. Deliberately, he encouraged women to come to Mount Sinai to do special work under him. Soon he had what was called his "harem"—Dr. Anne Topper, Dr. Margit (Mitzi) Freund, Dr. Rose Spiegel, Dr. Camille Kereszturi, and to each one of them he gave a push toward important research.

He did not neglect the men, and Dr. Karelitz among others, was spurred into an ardent creativeness.

Before Dr. Schick came, all of the blood studies and the allergic investigations (outside of Murray Peshkin's specialty), and metabolism tests and studies were made in the laboratories of the adult departments. It was not considered necessary to have a metabolist or a hematologist, just for children. Béla changed all that. He watched his "harem" and his nice young interns very carefully, then he said to one: "You are my metabolism expert," and to another: "I want you to specialize in hematology."

For Dr. Margit Freund's work in hematology they needed a special machine. Dr. Schick bought one for her out of his own pocket. "It is important," he explained. "The study of children's blood diseases is not the same as that of adults. We pediatricians must develop our own specialists in that field."

For Dr. Anne Topper, he had an idea. One day while they were making the rounds of the ward, they stopped at the bedside of a child who was convalescing from pneumonia. Dr. Schick said to all of them, but most pointedly to Dr. Topper: "I've noticed that in these pneumonia convalescents, the pulse is always very slow. I wonder whether it would have any relation to the basal metabolism?"

Dr. Topper, small, dark and extremely attractive, caught the fact that the question was particularly for her. She had shown some interest in metabolism before. His question was all she needed to get her started. She studied the basal metabolic rate in every case of a child convalescing from pneumonia. The work stretched over a long period of time but Dr. Schick never lost interest in it.

He taught her, as he taught the others, to dare to observe

everything, no matter how trivial; to constantly ask "why?" —"how?"—to watch carefully no matter how many tedious and tiring hours it took. They frequently discussed her findings. When she was finished, Dr. Schick insisted it be written and published. She did the rough draft of it, brought it to him for criticism; they worked over it together and when it was published it carried both their names.

This was not the case of a great man stealing credit from an unknown girl. Far from it. Dr. Schick had contributed a great deal to her research; his name on the paper insured that it would catch the attention of the medical world.

With Dr. Camille Kereszturi he was to do research into tuberculosis, although there were no infectious diseases at Mount Sinai. It all happened because one day Dr. Schick received a letter from Hungarian-born Camille. Could she come to America and work for him? He was delighted and told her to come right away.

He had no idea that she was almost penniless and expecting some sort of small salary from him. When he found that she had cut all ties in Hungary, that she was in a strange land almost without funds and living on ice cream because the sugar gave her energy, he was horrified.

There was no money at Mount Sinai appropriated for her, but he helped her get two jobs, both part time. One of these was at Sea-View Hospital, on Staten Island for tubercular patients. It was an easy next step, when Camille found that there was no qualified consulting pediatrician there at Sea-View, that Dr. Schick should be asked to take that job, too. He accepted; without pay, of course.

At six-thirty one morning every week he would accompany Camille to Staten Island by ferry. He would work there as long as he could, take the ferry back, catch a bus and be on time to start his usual day's work at Mount Sinai.

He also accepted the invitation to become the regular lecturer at Columbia University as Clinical Professor of Diseases of Children. Later on, he was to add hospital after hospital to his busy days, visiting them as consulting pediatrician.

Dr. Schick stuck to his resolve, handling private patients only when other pediatricians or doctors called upon him for special and difficult consultations. Then they had to fix the fee—he would either not ask anything or much too little.

Yet somehow he found the time to call on Cathy. Sometimes he would have to ask her to wait for him at restaurants near Columbia University or near Mount Sinai Hospital so that they could snatch an hour together. Then she would watch for him. Her sparkling brown eyes would soften when they caught sight of him.

The years had been kind to Béla Schick. He had grown into a handsome, distinguished-looking man. His thick hair was touched with gray, which made a striking contrast to his very dark, thick, arched eyebrows. His mouth was the most expressive part of his face. It was full, but disciplined. Years and years of speaking softly and tenderly to children had given it sweetness, which was there even if he were speaking of the weather.

Cathy would watch him coming, proud that this man loved her. She had no idea of the richness she was adding to his lonely life.

"Aren't you ever homesick for Austria?" she asked him once.

"Very often, when I first came; not so often now," he

smiled at her. "I have applied for my American citizenship. Did I tell you?"

"No. I'm glad," she answered.

His 'harem'—though not in love with him, but fiercely devoted to him—caught wind of the romance. They discussed it among themselves. This Cathy Fries, who was she? She was not even a pediatrician! She was of a well-to-do family; could she ever accept Dr. Schick's contemptuous attitude toward money? She was sixteen years younger; could she appreciate him?

Cathy could have answered yes to all these questions, if she had known then that they were being asked. She found out later, when all the women doctors became her good friends.

Perhaps she could not understand the technicalities of his medical language and research, but she wanted to be his wife, not his assistant. She had no desire to be in his profession or compete with him. She just wanted to help him.

A year and a half had passed. It was time for him to make the promised visit home to his mother. Unknown to any but Cathy's parents, it was arranged that she should follow on the next boat and become acquainted with Mrs. Schick and Richard and Frieda and Ilona. She was at last to meet Dr. Pirquet.

It was the summer of 1925. He left America with a feeling that he had struck roots there. He had done important work and had encouraged others to do the same. He was arranging, now, to get a scholarship so that the extremely bright Dr. Samuel Karelitz could study abroad.

This, then, was a well-deserved holiday for him.

When he met Cathy at the train in Graz, all his doubts vanished. This was the girl he wanted to marry. She brought a feeling of the free and independent spirit of America, yet she adapted well to old-fashioned Graz.

With Béla's mother she discussed his liking for good, simple food, his preference for a little sweet white wine with his dinner. She learned how to make *Linzer torte*, his favorite dessert. Together, they despaired over the fact that he would not wear a coat or hat even in the wintertime. She could listen forever to Richard's and Frieda's and Ilona's stories of Béla's childhood.

They went on to Vienna. She met Dr. Pirquet. "I have never seen him so happy," Dr. Pirquet told her. "I have never seen a young woman so radiant," he told Béla.

Watching Cathy and Clemens together, Béla knew that he was a lucky man. It was a rare thing for two such friends as he and Clemens Pirquet to have minds which so perfectly complemented each other; one supplying always what the other lacked. Now he was to have the great good fortune of marrying a woman whose heart and emotions were the other perfect complement to his.

When the holiday was over, he and Cathy sailed for New York. They were met at the dock by friends who were surprised and delighted to see them together. The secret was out. Their engagement was known.

On the third of December, 1925, they were married. They set up housekeeping in the same tiny two-room apartment where Béla had lived since coming to New York.

Mrs. Béla Schick cheerfully adapted to the apartment and to other attitudes and habits of her husband. She did the shopping and cooking and took care of the apartment, with no complaint that they could have afforded a maid. She bought her clothes in bargain basements. When they dined in a res-

taurant with another couple and Béla insisted upon the others
paying their own way, down to halving the tip, she understood him. This habit of his annoyed some people, since they
knew he could afford to play host. During intermission at the
theater he would refuse a cigarette if he thought he would not
have time to smoke it all and would have to waste it by throwing it away.

Cathy understood. He had suffered privation so long, had
scrimped and saved, and had seen so many people starving in
Vienna for the lack of a few pennies that he had a horror of
extravagance.

She knew that if there were something she really needed
and wanted, her husband would have made any sacrifice to
get it for her. At Christmastime, she saw him surprise all the
young, struggling interns in the hospitals where he worked
by buying and bringing them the kind of presents that were
just what they needed most. Every Christmas she would drive
him to the houses and apartments on his list while he struggled
up steps and into elevators to take radios and suitcases and
books to his "young people." She saw him dig into his own
pocket time and time again to buy equipment for his department at Mount Sinai.

So these penny-pinching habits of his did not bother her.
She would not have changed him in that respect. She did
make other profound alterations in his life: she taught him to
enjoy theaters and art museums, picnics and parties, the com-
pany of people who were not necessarily doctors. Cathy
Schick had a zest for laughter and fun and nonsense. So did
Béla; he simply needed her encouragement to enjoy himself.

The next four years were extremely happy ones for Dr.
Schick. Under his prodding the Pediatrics Department at

Mount Sinai soon became a model in the United States. He developed pediatric specialists among his own staff. There had never been newborn babies in the department; they had always been in the obstetric ward. Now, for special cases, he had cubicles built for the newly born. Gradually he was getting across the idea that pediatrics must concern itself with the child from the moment of birth until adulthood.

The Schick test, slowly but surely, was gaining acceptance. It was finding approval in the medical world. That must come first, he knew. Then the public must be informed and educated to it.

Letters from Austria brought good news. Dr. Pirquet was rising in the esteem and in the affection of his countrymen. He was working tirelessly at the hospital; outside of it, in politics, campaigning for public health and social reforms. Members of Dr. Schick's own family were doing well. Richard had taken his wife and settled in Italy, where he was prospering. Ilona stayed home with their mother; Frieda was happy with her husband and daughter. Béla's half sister Serena wrote that her daughter Erna had studied to become a teacher and was thinking of getting married.

Then in 1927 came the turning point which would fulfill his dreams of conquering diphtheria. A great campaign was started in New York City. Dr. Shirley W. Wynne, Commissioner of Health, championed it. Public committees were formed with names of prominent people to sponsor it.

Against his will, Dr. Schick was forced into the limelight for the campaign. He was urged to take part in it by Dr. Abraham Zingher, who was now Director of New York City Research Laboratories. Dr. Zingher made it clear to him that this was a crucial test, a city-wide campaign of education, and it was no time for modesty. His name must be used; he must speak and write.

He became head of the Technical Consultation Board of the Diphtheria Commission. He wrote press releases. He was photographed and interviewed. He was quoted. His picture appeared on posters under which were the startling words in bold type: NO CHILD NEED HAVE DIPHTHERIA.

This was an incredible concept to most people. Diphtheria seemed to be one of the natural, if tragic, hazards of childhood. Mothers and fathers in New York stopped to read the posters and wonder about it. They sat beside their radios, listening with fearful hope as Dr. Schick broadcast his message to them:

"The United States diphtheria record for 1927 was in round numbers one hundred thousand cases, with about ten thousand deaths. This means that ten thousand people died in the United States during 1927 from a disease which could have been avoided. What an amount of suffering, what an amount of sorrow, could have been spared the parents of these children if they had known that the disease could have been avoided. . . !"

Mothers and fathers, hearing this, looked at each other and thought of their own children and wondered if this man, speaking in what was now only a slight foreign accent, could possibly be telling the truth. They heard him describe the Schick test. They heard him explain how simple and easy it would be to find out exactly which children were immune and which needed the protection of an injection. Was this possible?

The schoolchildren brought home slips of paper for their parents to sign, giving permission for the Schick test. In all of New York City there were only a very few who refused. The publicity campaign had been successful, almost all mothers and fathers were finally convinced that there was nothing harmful in either the Schick test or in the injection, if it proved necessary to give one.

Doctors and nurses appeared at the schools on the appointed day. Naturally, the photographers and newspapermen gathered at the school where Dr. Béla Schick himself was to conduct the testing. They watched with amazement the simplicity and speed with which Dr. Schick, talking and joking with each child, made a tiny, tiny injection under the skin of the arm . . . almost a scratch.

Dr. Schick's attention was directed to the children, not the newspapermen. If they wanted to listen, too, that was all right with him.

"Now, you see what I am doing?" he would ask the child. "It doesn't hurt, does it? I want you to tell your mommy and daddy and your teacher and the nurse who will be coming here every day for a while, to watch that arm. If nothing happens then you are immune, which means you couldn't have diphtheria even if you wanted to. If a red spot develops then you will be given three injections of what we call toxin-antitoxin—don't laugh, or I won't be able to make this little scratch on your arm—I know it is a funny, big word. But you must have it once a week for three weeks and I promise it won't hurt you at all. You would have to have those injections because otherwise you might get very sick and not be able to play like other little girls."

The children understood. For days afterward they matched arms with one another. Those who did show the red spots were anxious for the injections so that they would not get sick.

The antidiphtheria campaign in New York was spread over five years, from 1927 to 1932, catching each new group of children as they came of school age, and spreading farther and farther until every single school was included. By the end of 1932 it was no longer necessary to conduct such a strenuous campaign. Parents and doctors were convinced. It became the most ordinary thing in the world to see to it that a child automatically had a Schick test at an early age.

At the same time the education and understanding of it was extending to every part of the United States.

Diphtheria, one of the most deadly, crippling diseases, was on its way out. This was Béla Schick's greatest fulfillment. Four men had made it possible: Friedrich Löffler and Edwin Klebs had discovered the diphtheria bacillus; Emil von Behring had found the diphtheria antitoxin; Béla Schick had proved a test whereby immunity became possible, not for just a single individual, but for thousands upon the same hour and day and week.

In the year of 1929 he could look about him and see great accomplishments. Pediatrics was no longer treated with contempt but with respect. Every childhood disease was the subject of intensive study in order to find the cure and prevention. The special problems of children were no longer ignored. It was now known what to expect of each year's growth and development. Even the mental processes were being examined. Child psychology was born.

Great international pediatric conferences were being held, which Dr. and Mrs. Schick attended every year. More often than not, he was one of the principal speakers. Every country tried to outdo the others in showering honors upon him.

He was the consulting pediatrician at the Willard Parker

Hospital, and the New York Infirmary for Women and Children. Publishers wanted translations of his earlier works. He was besieged with invitations to speak at functions.

Life, in 1929, seemed secure and richly rewarding and untroubled. He was not prepared for the great tragedy that befell him.

Dr. Pirquet was dead.

10

The first shock of the news was followed by a worse one, when a letter from Vienna reached Dr. Schick with more details. Clemens von Pirquet and his wife Maria had committed suicide together by swallowing cyanide of potassium.

Why? It was incredible! Béla's great friend was a doctor and as such he valued life. He did not despise it. What would have made him do such a thing?

Béla reread the letter, seeing the story between the lines. Dr. Pirquet had been persuaded to run for the presidency of the Republic of Austria. The idea was not as strange as it sounded. He was extremely likable, idealistic and incorruptible. He was also an able administrator. Around him, many parties might have united. But 1929 was a time of turmoil in Austria. Violent bands of violent men were using those times to come to power. They hated the ideals of Dr. Pirquet.

Suddenly he was dropped as a presidential candidate, after throwing himself with all his heart and nerves, into the campaign. His wife was ill. There must have seemed little for them to live for.

Béla knew that Clemens von Pirquet was not personally ambitious. A personal defeat would have meant little to him; but to see his country following bad leaders was too much. As sensitive a man as Dr. Pirquet would suffer for that. He would have been in despair, wondering if he had thrown away years of political effort instead of devoting those years to the hospital.

Even after the first shock and grief were over, Béla could not forget it. All Mrs. Schick could do was to stand by with sympathy and understanding. His sufferings were intense. Memories overwhelmed him. He remembered those early days in Vienna; those eager, exciting days when he and Dr. Pirquet had worked in the finest of partnerships. He remembered the nights, by candlelight, bending over the beds of sick children —the hours in the library writing together. All was gone. Once he and Dr. Pirquet had stood in the rain on the steps of the diphtheria building at St. Anna, too engrossed in their discussion to know it was raining.

Now the rain beat on Clemens' lonely grave in Austria.

Except to Cathy, Dr. Schick did not show his anguish. He did the one last thing he could for his friend. He sat down and wrote for a Berlin pediatric journal, which would be published in Austria as well, a three-thousand-word memorial to Dr. Pirquet.

Luckily, Dr. Schick's work forced him out of his grief. The only legacy his friend had left him was their old responsibility for children and he would not neglect this.

He was one of the founders of the American Academy of Pediatrics. Very shortly after Dr. Pirquet's death this organization held an important round-table discussion on allergy, led by Dr. Schick. He brought the young Dr. Murray Peshkin with him.

At this meeting Dr. Schick went back in time to those early days when Clemens von Pirquet had been the first to use the word "allergy." He discussed this pioneer work. Of course, there had been other pioneers. One of the marvels of medicine was the fact that men would be doing research on the same subject at the same time, perhaps from a different angle, without any knowledge of each other's work. No one could deny that Dr. Pirquet was the first man to use the word "allergy."

But at this round-table meeting, Dr. Schick moved from the past to the present and then to the future. He praised the work of Dr. Peshkin and others like him who were enlarging the concept of allergy to allergic diseases of asthma, hay fever, extreme sensitivity to certain proteins in dust and food and pollens . . . and insect stings.

It had been a long, long way from the allergic reaction the twelve-year-old boy Béla Schick had received from a bee sting, to this modern analysis of why and how and what to do about it.

This new branch of medical science, devoted to allergic diseases and reactions, was growing in leaps and bounds. Those at the round-table discussion foresaw the day when entire hospitals and laboratories would be built for only the allergic sufferers.

So Béla Schick put his sorrow over his dead friend aside and went on working. Sometimes Mrs. Schick saw the shadow which haunted his eyes, but he spoke of Clemens Pirquet more and more easily as time went on.

He had been accepted, long ago, as a Fellow of the New York Academy of Medicine. He had lectured to them on "Certain Aspects of Tuberculosis in Infancy." Everything and anything relating to diseases in children interested him. Over a period of years the articles he wrote himself or co-authored were proof of his wide knowledge:

"Reorganization of Nutrition Work to Save Food Waste in Children's Departments" . . . "Observation of the Nutritional Effect of Subcutaneous Oil Injections," with Margaret Fries. . . . "Concentrated Feeding" . . . "The Predisposing Factor in Diphtheria" . . . "The Basal Metabolism after Pneumonia," with Anne Topper. . . . "Tuberculosis in Childhood" . . . "Effect of Tonsillectomy and of Adenoidectomy on Di-Immunity," with Anne Topper. . . . "Parenteral BCG Vaccine," with W. H. Park and Camille Kereszturi. . . . "Treatment of Alimentary Toxicosis," with Samuel Karelitz. . . .

On and on, year after year, the remarkable Dr. Schick contributed to medicine and pediatrics.

Mrs. Schick had one certain way of making him relax. Every year there would be an international conference of pediatricians, held in some big capital of the world. She bought a car and left it in Europe. Then, when Dr. Schick had made his speech and listened to others and the conference was over, they would gather into the car such friends as Dr. Topper or Dr. Kereszturi and be off on a holiday tour. Oh, there was always an excuse for it—a hospital to see or a leading pediatrician to visit—but Mrs. Schick made certain that it was a holiday, too.

They would picnic alongside the roads. Dr. Schick loved this. Bread and cheese and sausage and apples by the side of a stream or under the shade of trees to keep off the sun, was much better than all the grand receptions and dignified social affairs given for them in Paris or Copenhagen or London.

Mrs. Schick did all the driving. He could drive but not to

anyone else's satisfaction. He was apt to start thinking of some difficult medical case and forget what he was doing.

In 1933 came an honor to Dr. Béla Schick which meant more to him than all the medals and awards he was accumulating from societies and academies. He was presented with an enormous leather-bound album, signed by *one million* New York children, in deep gratitude to the man who had saved those one million lives—and others—from the threat of diphtheria.

The ceremony was a simple and touching one. Dr. Schick took the book from the hands of one of those children. He turned the leaves and looked at the scrawled, childish, handwritten names and his eyes blurred with tears.

But in Germany very different kinds of ceremonies were taking place. Vicious, brutal men in brown shirts were gathering around the city of Berlin, marching in the streets, raising their arms in salute—when those same arms were not beating up helpless men, women and children. Adolph Hitler had come to power. One of the essentials of his taking power and holding it was the cruel lie, repeated over and over until people were mesmerized by it, that the Jews were responsible for all the troubles of the world. His determined boast was that the Jews would be eliminated in Germany.

Dr. Béla Schick was so wrapped up in the world of pediatrics that he did not really understand at that time what was going on. Few people in America did. Dr. Pirquet's death had been a warning, but it was not in Béla Schick's nature to see the substance of evil, when evil was still a shadow.

He worried over what might be happening in his country. Yet the international conferences were still being held. The doctors in Austria and Germany seemed to work as they had before, without too much trouble.

Rumors of persecution and of concentration camps began to come to America, from refugees from Germany. Jewish doctors, scientists and professors smuggled out letters to their friends outside, telling of the pressure put upon them to teach and practice according to Nazi rule—if they were allowed to practice at all. Dr. Schick was at last seriously alarmed.

Even so, the full realization of how deep and far the Nazi poison had spread did not come home to him until he experienced it himself.

Dr. and Mrs. Schick were traveling in Italy in 1938. They had finished with the business of conferences and meetings and were looking forward to the pleasure of visiting with Richard and his wife, who had settled in Rome.

Tired, hungry, feeling the need for baths and rest before they saw Richard, Dr. and Mrs. Schick checked into a Rome hotel. Several times before they had stayed in this particular hotel and had liked it, as they liked most of the friendly Italians.

This time they were barely in their room and unpacked when the manager knocked on the door. He was extremely sorry, but the Schicks must leave.

"Why?" asked Béla, in amazement. "Your hotel is not full. We have stayed here before. Why must we leave?"

The manager was embarrassed; he looked wretched and fearful, but he was determined. He urged the Schicks to leave quietly and not to force him to make an explanation. When they insisted upon knowing why, he told them that a German Nazi was staying in the hotel and he would not tolerate Jews under the same roof with him.

The manager was a coward but Dr. Schick could hardly blame him. All of Italy, including Mussolini, had gradually come under Hitler's domination. Anti-Semitism had never before gained much of a foothold in Italy; the Germans brought it with them; now it was nearly as bad as in Germany.

It was a shock to Béla. He hadn't realized how far and how deep the poison had spread. When he and Cathy reached Richard's house in Rome, they begged him to leave Italy and come to America.

"I shall be all right," he told them, "but get Mamma and Frieda and Ilona and Serena out, with their families. It isn't too late. Austria has gone Nazi. But so far Austrians are being treated as partners in the German Reich, not slaves as those in other territories are. It is still possible for Jews to buy their way out. Help them, Béla."

Béla did not need to be urged. He was not allowed to go to Austria, but once back in the United States he applied for the affidavits he would need to assure the American government that his family would be supported by him in New York if they came. He had long ago become a citizen of the United States. He filled out the affidavits and wrote to his family that they should immediately begin whatever process was needed to escape.

Before it could take place, in January of 1939, his mother died. She was eighty years old. Much and dearly as Béla loved her, his sorrow for her death was tempered with a feeling that she would have preferred to die now than to tear up her roots in Graz. She was too old to become an American.

He bent all efforts to get his sisters away from the Nazis. Frieda wrote, eagerly, that she wanted to come but there was a difficulty: her husband was Hungarian and, therefore, her daughter was half Hungarian. They had been informed that the quota of Hungarian immigrants allowed to enter America was already filled, though there was still room for Austrians. Could Béla do something to persuade the American government to forget its quotas and allow Hungarian refugees to come, before they were all killed?

He tried. It was agony to find out that such quotas had been set by Congress; that it would take a special act of Congress to change it; that nothing could be done just for one or two individuals.

The time was running out. While Dr. Schick was still pursuing every possible avenue to help his sister and her husband and child, suddenly it was too late. There were no answers to his letters to Austria. Frieda—too loyal to leave her husband and daughter—had vanished.

Ilona he saved, and Serena's daughter, Erna, and Erna's husband. That was all. As the horror of war mounted, the world learned of such things as concentration camps and the mass extermination of Jews.

In September, when Hitler attacked Poland, Richard died. His death was from natural causes but Béla knew well that whatever his brother's illness, it had been aggravated by his worry over his sisters.

For the first time, in a life devoted to the care and the love of humanity, Béla Schick allowed himself to hate. No one had ever seen him angry before, but as information began to trickle through the tight fist of Germany, he learned that his sister, her husband and daughter were in a concentration camp; when he heard of renowned doctors who had been killed or tortured or had committed suicide, his anger tore aside the quiet fabric of his life.

Wherever he could, he spoke against the Nazis and told what they were doing. He and Cathy worked tirelessly to help get other refugees out, as Hitler conquered nation after nation.

Dr. Schick was in a position to make his voice heard and to warn America of the danger to itself. He had received the Addingham Gold Medal, from Britain, for "the most valuable discovery for relieving pain and suffering in humanity." In January, 1941, the annual Forum of Allergy in Indianapolis, Indiana, presented him with their Gold Medal for his pioneer work in allergy. He was considered by all pediatricians as their dean and leader.

The New York Academy of Medicine's Gold Medal had been given to him on the occasion of the twenty-fifth anniversary of his discovery of the Schick test. To that banquet had come renowned medical professors, pediatricians, and doctors from all over the world to do him homage.

He spoke at these times on two subjects: "Save the world from disease—save the world from the tyranny of Hitlerism." He worked with the United Hospital Campaign Committee and with the Red Cross. He willingly cooperated and gave time to the State Department to help rescue refugees.

The year after America entered the war, Dr. Béla Schick reached his sixty-fifth birthday. It was the rule at Mount Sinai that heads of departments must resign at that age. He did so, but was almost immediately asked to continue in his role there as consulting pediatrician. At the same time he extended his work instead of diminishing it. He took on the consulting pediatrician's responsibilities for Beth-El Hospital in the Bronx. He gave teaching time to the medical division of Yeshiva

University, later to be renamed the Albert Einstein College of Medicine.

When the war was over and the search for survivors began, he learned the full extent of his personal tragedy. Frieda, her husband and daughter had all been killed in concentration camps. Nor was that all: over thirty members of his family—cousins, aunts and uncles—had perished the same way.

Dr. Schick was nearly seventy. He was still an active pediatrician in hospitals. He added to his work another resolve—for his own satisfaction he would search for the answer to war and hatreds and human misery.

With Mrs. Schick always at his side, after the war he journeyed to many countries. They saw the new Israel and marveled that people so crushed by the Nazis could emigrate to this new land and build homes, hospitals, schools and new cities with little more than their stout hearts and high hopes. It seemed to Dr. Schick that he had rarely seen a place where people loved children more.

They went to the Soviet Union and came away highly approving of the medical progress there. They were convinced that the people of this nation sincerely wanted peace.

Everywhere they found the same desire for peace and security and progress. Dr. Schick took some comfort from this, but it seemed to him that the germs of greed and prejudice and old hatreds should be hunted down, identified, stamped out with the same vigor as men hunted for the germ of diphtheria or scarlet fever. If there was an antitoxin for war, it was to be found in social and economic reforms where no man or nation might profit from the misery of others.

At the advanced age of seventy, Dr. Schick was to surprise many of his colleagues with his thinking. It amused and delighted him to find he was considered a political radical. Men were supposed to grow conservative as they grew older, but not Dr. Schick.

There was nothing wrong with him physically, either. He went on with his observations, steadily supplying medical journals with new articles on every kind of disease of childhood. He was creating a vast reservoir of knowledge for other doctors to draw upon. His subjects ranged from allergy in rheumatic disease, to the use of tea prepared from the needles of pine trees, against the disease of scurvy. He wrote about the placental transmission of mumps and streptococcus. His interests never flagged.

Three days a week he went to Beth-El Hospital, where he was still consulting pediatrician.

There his early-morning arrival was awaited with joy. The elevator man greeted him, smiling. If Dr. Schick had been to a banquet the night before he always saved the after-dinner cigars for the elevator man, and their presentation became a little ritual between them.

The staff was waiting and so were the children. To them, Dr. Schick was no frightening man in a white coat. He was the one person who knew how they wanted to talk and could talk their language; who knew how they wanted to play and could invent games for them. They never realized that when he took one of them on his lap and petted him, he was actually giving him a physical examination.

Though world-prominent he didn't look it. He still refused to wear an overcoat or hat, even in the midst of winter. Once when he got off the subway in the Bronx and walked to Dr. Alla Dunewitz's office-apartment, she was waiting at the garage door for him. It was the custom for him to meet her there and drive with her to Beth-El Hospital. This day she was laughing.

"Dr. Schick, you really must get an overcoat," she said to him. "You give the wrong impression to people. Yesterday, the man who looks after my yard and car and garage said to me: 'Doctor, who is that poor man who comes here? The one who is so poor he can't afford a coat or a hat'?"

Béla laughed, too. "I'm seventy-two and never sick," he boasted. "I sleep like a child, eat well and never have to go to see a doctor. Am I lucky!"

When they arrived at the hospital they found it was more or less a typical day. Dr. Schick came three times a week but he always remembered every child's name and every case history. Now, with the rest of the staff, he made his rounds as he had been doing in hospitals for nearly fifty years.

There was the poor child with the abscess of the brain. There was the three-year-old with meningitis, a brave little one who always smiled and was a pet of the nurses. Two of the children had acute rheumatic fever; four had heart conditions. One small boy suffered with nephrosis. A little girl had been badly burned in a kitchen fire, when she had tried to light the gas stove by herself.

Beside this child Béla lingered. The healing process was going well. The little girl's face would not be scarred. Nevertheless, she had been terribly frightened and had lived for a long time with pain and suffering. He thought it important to stay and talk with her, to find out if she still had bad dreams or if she was gaining confidence once more that the world was a secure place for her.

Back of him the staff doctors fidgeted. Dr. Dunewitz sighed.

She and the others were pressed for time because there was always so much to do in the hospital, but there was no rushing Dr. Schick when he thought a child needed him.

After the rounds were over he disappeared. He was on his way, as usual, to the ward where the new babies were. He had never lost interest in the premature babies, probably because he, himself, had been a "preemie." The question as to why babies sometimes came too soon was still unanswered. Medical science was making progress but that had not been solved.

After he had checked up on the tiny babies in their specially warmed glass boxes, he returned that day to speak again to Dr. Dunewitz and invite her to spend her vacation at his summer home in Garrison, and to come to dinner that evening at their apartment.

Yes, it was the same two-and-a-half room apartment. They had bought a twenty-six acre farm near Garrison in Putnam County, New York State, but the frugal Dr. Schick saw no reason to give up his familiar quarters on East Eighty-fourth Street when he was in the city.

That night their guests, besides Dr. Dunewitz, included Dr. Anne Topper, Dr. Jerome Leopold and Dr. Bella Singer. After dinner they urged Béla to the piano where he played his favorites for them, even some of the newer and more modern works. When he thought he had played enough, Dr. Topper, now a distinguished doctor with a large practice, had a surprise for him. She was in the habit of writing poetry to amuse her friends and had written one, to the tune of Gilbert and Sullivan's *H.M.S. Pinafore*.

She would sing it but Béla must play the tune. So they began, but to Béla's surprise it was a song about him:

"When I was a lad in Hungary
I couldn't dance the czardas, or the bokonee,
My dancing had so many faults,
They sent me to Vienna to learn to waltz.
At waltzing I achieved such fame,
That assistant to Von Pirquet I soon became.
To Von Pirquet I felt so inferior,
I decided to investigate diphtheria.
I diligently pursued my quest,
Till by accident I found a new skin test.
The test it was named after me,
And that's why I received so much publicity.
My fame soon spread across the sea,
To Mount Sinai where there was a vacancy. . . .
In the kitchen I found such extravagant waste,
The garbage was enough to feed another place. . . .

There were more verses, but by this time they were all laughing so hard they had to stop singing. Mrs. Schick found the description of Béla as a waltz expert extremely funny. He had never learned to dance. The guests were delighted to have Dr. Topper poke a little fun at Béla's always-modest insistence that he was not the genius Von Pirquet was.

But it was the reference to his descent into the Mount Sinai kitchen that almost threw them into hysterics. In Dr. Schick's early days at Mount Sinai he had indeed gone into the kitchen of the Children's Department and he had indeed thrown everything into an uproar. The supervisor had been scandalized, the cooks were in tears, but Dr. Schick was relentless as he watched every spoonful that went into every dish. He checked the size and shape of every saucepan. He lifted the lids of the garbage cans and peered at them, muttering with shock under his breath.

Then had come a whole new routine. He had explained to them the N.E.M. method which he and Dr. Pirquet had devised in Vienna, which made sure that each child got his or her full meal, but allowed for no waste.

Pots and pans were found which were exactly the right size. Exact measurements were written down for the cooks to follow. Not a tray was carried into the children's wards which Dr. Schick did not investigate, until he could be sure that no food was going to be wasted or thrown away because too-lavish portions were cooked or served.

Busy as they were, the nurses might have rebelled at this extra work, but they would do anything for Dr. Schick. He treated them as equals. He said: "A good nurse in a hospital is a foundation for a good hospital" and they knew he appreciated everything they did.

That night in his apartment, Dr. Béla Schick looked about him at his wife and his friends, and he knew he had at last weathered the storm of his life and come into safe harbor.

He, who had been lonely for so long, had found the one perfect companion in Cathy Schick. He had come to America as a stranger; his adopted country had welcomed both him and his discoveries.

These friends of his were also his former students. They were not young any more, but all of them had done extremely well and some had even become famous in their own right.

It was not often given to a pioneer to see the completion of his work. He had—although as long as there was a single disease and a single sick child, he would not call it complete. Pediatrics was flourishing. Where there had been a handful of pediatricians in the world when Dr. Béla Schick became one, now there were thousands in nearly every country. Professor Escherich would have been proud.

And how proud Dr. Pirquet would have been if he had lived to see the great hospital out in Denver, just for asthmatic children! This was the work, especially, of Dr. Murray Peshkin.

He remembered his Uncle Sigismund who had inspired him to become a doctor. The book of medical knowledge was still not completely written. Dr. Schick looked forward to great advances in biochemistry, in understanding why babies were born prematurely, and in the conquering of many still little known viruses, especially measles.

Yes, there was still work to be done, but his own was nearly finished.

Though Dr. Schick, now in his eighties, is no longer active, he continues to be the recipient of honor after honor. Medals of gold come one month, medals of silver the next; his birthdays are honored both by medical men and distinguished leaders of New York City.

He has the important John Howland Medal of the American Pediatric Society; the Brith Sholom Humanitarian Award; the City of Hope Citation of Merit; the Abraham Jacobi Medal; the Allergy Medal; the Leeds Medal—he has plaques from the Sociedad Boliviana de Pediatrics; from the Muscular Dystrophy Association of America; from the Medical Society of New York for Distinguished and Exceptional Public Service . . . the listing of them all would be endless.

So would the list of societies which have made him a member, among them the American Pediatric Society, the Society for Experimental Biology and Medicine, the American Asso-

ciation of Immunologists, not to speak of the European asso-
ciations.

With the death of Mrs. Schick's parents, Cathy persuaded
her husband to move into the warmer, more comfortable and
spacious apartment which had been owned by the Fries family
for many years. Ilona has her apartment upstairs from them,
so that she can visit them often. His niece Erna can come there
on vacations; this daughter of his sister Serena has become a
citizen of America and a teacher in Omaha, Nebraska.

In this apartment he is surrounded by the treasures and
memories of his life, but what he mostly enjoys looking at are
the cabinets full of beautiful dolls and toys which he and
Cathy brought home from their travels.

Here doctors and leading figures of public life come to visit
and honor him. To some of them he is a saint; to others a living legend of the selfless, devoted doctor. To many he is the
great pioneer. To everyone—and especially to the children—
he is a friend.

INDEX

Index

185

About the Author

IRIS NOBLE grew up on a ranch in the Crow's Nest Pass between Canada's Alberta and British Columbia. Her parents were American and when she was eleven they moved to Oregon. After graduating from the University of Oregon, she moved to Los Angeles and got her first job as a secretary at station KFI-KECA. She left there to work for Fawcett Publications and later was publicity director for a theatre-restaurant. After her marriage she came to New York City where she did freelance writing. In recent years she has made her home in San Francisco and has been devoting herself to writing both in the field of biography and teenage fiction.